MATH TRAILBLAZERS™

Grade 4

Unit Resource Guide
Unit 8

Measuring Up:
An Assessment Unit

SECOND EDITION

A Mathematical Journey Using Science and Language Arts

KENDALL/HUNT PUBLISHING COMPANY
4050 Westmark Drive   Dubuque, Iowa 52002

A TIMS® Curriculum
University of Illinois at Chicago

UIC The University of Illinois
at Chicago

The original edition was based on work supported by the National Science Foundation under grant No. MDR 9050226 and the University of Illinois at Chicago. Any opinions, findings, and conclusions or recommendations expressed in this publication are those of the author(s) and do not necessarily reflect the views of the granting agencies.

LETTER HOME

Measuring Up: An Assessment Unit

Date: _____

Dear Family Member:

During this unit, your child will participate in activities that review and assess skills and concepts covered so far this year. Students will perform an experiment in which they investigate volume. They will work in groups to solve an open-response problem and write up their solutions. They will also solve review problems for homework, take a midyear test, and review their math portfolios.

You can help your child by following these suggestions:

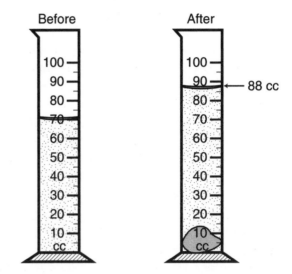

Students learn about measuring volume with graduated cylinders.

- Ask your child to explain this picture. The drawing on the left shows a graduated cylinder with water in it. The drawing on the right shows the same graduated cylinder after a lump of clay has been added. Why is the water level higher in the picture on the right? What is the volume of the clay?

- Play *Operation Target*. This game reviews the math facts and requires logical thinking. Your child will bring home the rules for this game. Since it does not require a game board or other materials, this is a good game to play when you have a few free minutes together.

- Use the *Triangle Flash Cards* to help your child study a small group of 8–10 multiplication facts each night. Your child will take a test on all the multiplication facts at the end of this unit.

- Ask your child to tell you about the best piece of work in his or her portfolio.

Thank you for helping with our review.

Sincerely,

_____

UNIT OUTLINE

Measuring Up:
An Assessment Unit

Pacing Suggestions

This unit includes a variety of review and assessment activities that provide opportunities for teachers to assess individual growth in mathematics. Students continue learning as they apply concepts and skills in new contexts.

- Lesson 4 *Review Problems* is an optional lesson. It is a set of problems that reviews skills and concepts from the first seven units and helps students prepare for the *Midyear Test* in Lesson 6. The problems can be assigned for homework. Lesson 4 is also appropriate for use by a substitute teacher.

- Lessons 1–3 provide connections to science. Students can review volume measurement in Lesson 1 *Volume* or collect data for the lab in Lesson 3 *Volume vs. Number* during science time. Part 3 of Lesson 1 is an optional activity that uses material from Grade 3 to review measuring volume by displacement. If your students have had opportunities to measure volume in Grades 2 and 3, omit this activity.

- Lesson 8 *Facts I Know: Multiplication and Division Facts* completes students' review of the multiplication facts with an inventory test of all the multiplication facts. (See DPP Bit U.) This lesson also begins the study and assessment of the division facts that will continue in the Daily Practice and Problems and Home Practice in Units 9–16. All students should continue working on new concepts and skills while they are learning the division facts. Because the math facts program is closely linked to the recommended schedule for teaching lessons, classrooms that differ significantly from the suggested pacing will need to make accommodations in order to ensure that students receive a consistent program of math facts practice and assessment throughout the year. The *Grade 4 Facts Resource Guide* outlines a schedule for the study of math facts in classrooms that move much more slowly through lessons than is recommended in the Lesson Guides. For more information, see the TIMS Tutor: *Math Facts* in the *Teacher Implementation Guide*.

Components Key: SG = Student Guide, DAB = Discovery Assignment Book, AB = Adventure Book, URG = Unit Resource Guide, and DPP = Daily Practice and Problems

	Sessions	Description	Supplies
LESSON 1			
Volume SG pages 216–220 DAB pages 101–106 URG pages 25–41 DPP A–B	1–2	**ACTIVITY:** Students discuss volume and review methods for measuring volume. This lesson includes an optional review section for students who have not taken part in volume activities in previous grades. Students review the multiplication facts for homework.	• eyedroppers • containers of water • rulers • centimeter cubes • packs • 250-cc graduated cylinders • small objects to measure by displacement

	Sessions	Description	Supplies
LESSON 2 **Fill It First** SG pages 221–224 DAB page 107 URG pages 42–47 DPP C–D	1	**GAME:** Students find volume by displacement using graduated cylinders. They play a game in which teams of students compete to predict the rise in water level as marbles are added to graduated cylinders. Homework in the *Student Guide* reviews the order of operations.	• clear plastic spinners or paper clips and pencils • 100-cc graduated cylinders • marbles • eyedroppers • paper towels • containers of water
LESSON 3 **Volume vs. Number** SG pages 225–229 DAB pages 109–111 URG pages 48–58 DPP E–J	3–4	**ASSESSMENT LAB:** Students collect, organize, and graph data to solve problems involving volume. They review drawing best-fit lines and using graphs to make predictions for homework.	• 250-cc graduated cylinders • marbles • plastic spheres • eyedroppers • paper towels • rulers • containers of water • containers for marbles
LESSON 4 **Review Problems** SG pages 230–231 URG pages 59–61	1	**– OPTIONAL ACTIVITY–** **OPTIONAL ACTIVITY:** Students solve problems that review skills and concepts from previous units.	• calculators • rulers
LESSON 5 **Hour Walk** URG pages 62–75 DPP K–L	1–2	**ASSESSMENT ACTIVITY:** Using the student rubrics as guides, students solve a problem and communicate the solution. They estimate the number of steps they will take if they walk for one hour. **ASSESSMENT PAGE:** *Hour Walk,* Unit Resource Guide, page 74.	• calculators • stopwatches

	Sessions	Description	Supplies
LESSON 6 **Midyear Test** URG pages 76–87 DPP M–P	2	**ASSESSMENT ACTIVITY:** Students take a short-item test that assesses skills and concepts studied since the beginning of the year. **ASSESSMENT PAGE:** *Midyear Test,* Unit Resource Guide, pages 81–86.	• rulers • calculators • square-inch tiles
LESSON 7 **Midyear Experiment and Portfolio Review** SG pages 232–233 DAB pages 113–114 URG pages 88–94 DPP Q–T	2	**ASSESSMENT ACTIVITY:** Students review the experiments completed during the first half of the school year. They then organize and review their portfolios.	• portfolios • collection folders
LESSON 8 **Facts I Know: Multiplication and Division Facts** SG pages 234–236 DAB pages 115–119 URG pages 95–101 DPP U–V	1	**ASSESSMENT ACTIVITY:** Students take the *Multiplication Facts Inventory Test* and learn to use the *Triangle Flash Cards* to practice the division facts.	• envelopes

---

CONNECTIONS

A current list of connections is available at www.mathtrailblazers.com.

Literature   **Suggested Title**

- *Aesop's Fables.* Compiled and illustrated by Jerry Pinkney. SeaStar Books, New York, 2000.

Software

- *Graph Master* allows students to organize data and create graphs.
- *Kid Pix* allows students to create their own illustrations.
- *Math Mysteries Measurement* develops multistep problem solving with distance, weight, and capacity.

PREPARING FOR UPCOMING LESSONS

In Unit 9, students will cut up boxes to explore three-dimensional shapes. Have students bring in boxes such as cereal boxes, gelatin boxes, and cracker boxes that are relatively easy to cut with scissors. Students will also need juice boxes (which are not easy to cut up) for use in Unit 9.

Place three-dimensional solids in a learning center for students to explore prior to beginning Unit 9.

BACKGROUND

Measuring Up: An Assessment Unit

The goals of this unit parallel those of Unit 2 *Geometric Investigations: A Baseline Assessment Unit* and Unit 16 *Assessing Our Learning*. Both units include activities that will give you information about students' mathematical knowledge. The unit also includes instruction on volume and other topics.

Each of the unit's activities will give you a different piece of assessment information. As students work on the lab *Volume vs. Number,* you can assess their skills in collecting, organizing, graphing, and analyzing data. The lab will also give you an opportunity to evaluate students as they work in groups to complete a long task. *Hour Walk* is a shorter task that assesses students' abilities to devise and carry out a problem-solving plan and then communicate the solution. *The Midyear Test* is made up of short items. It assesses skills and concepts studied in the first eight units. Students review and add to their portfolios. The final lesson includes an inventory test of the multiplication facts. These assessments will complement daily observations and give a balanced picture of your students' progress since the beginning of the year. For more information about the overall assessment program, refer to the Assessment section in the *Teacher Implementation Guide.*

Notes on Volume

Students using *Math Trailblazers*™ have had many experiences with volume beginning in kindergarten. In second grade, they compared the volumes of containers by counting the number of objects that fill the containers. In third grade, students compared containers by measuring the amount of water in the containers using a graduated cylinder. They also found the volume of objects made with connecting cubes by counting cubic units. In both second and third grades, they used a graduated cylinder to measure the volume of objects by displacement.

This unit begins with a review of volume for all students. For those students who have not had many experiences with volume, one of the lessons from third grade, *Estimating and Measuring Volume,* has been included as an optional part of Lesson 1. Following these introductory activities, students further explore volume by playing a game and conducting an experiment. For further information on volume, see the TIMS Tutor: *The Concept of Volume* in the *Teacher Implementation Guide.*

Review

This unit contains several activities that will help students review concepts they have explored. Students will review the multiplication facts. They will play the game *Operation Target* to review the order of operations and complete a homework assignment called *Predicting Prices* where they fit lines through data points to make predictions.

Resources

- *Aesop's Fables*. Compiled and illustrated by Jerry Pinkney. SeaStar Books, New York, 2000.
- Brownell, W. "The Evaluation of Learning in Arithmetic." In W.D. Reeve (Ed.), *The National Council of Teachers of Mathematics Sixteenth Yearbook: Arithmetic in General Education.* Bureau of Publications, Teachers College, Columbia University, New York, 1941.
- National Research Council. *Knowing What Students Know: The Science and Design of Educational Assessment.* Committee on the Foundations of Assessment. J. Pelligrino, N. Chudowsky, and R. Glaser eds. National Academy Press, Washington, DC, 2001.
- Stenmark, J.K. *Mathematics Assessment: Myths, Models, Good Questions, and Practical Suggestions.* The National Council of Teachers of Mathematics, Reston, VA, 1991.
- U.S. Bureau of the Census, *Statistical Abstract of the United States: 2001. The National Data Book* (121st edition), Washington, DC, 2001.

Assessment Indicators

- Can students collect, organize, graph, and analyze data?
- Can students make and interpret point graphs?
- Can students draw and interpret best-fit lines?
- Can students use patterns in data tables and graphs to make predictions?
- Can students measure volume by displacement?
- Can students solve open-response problems and communicate solution strategies?
- Do students demonstrate fluency with the multiplication facts?
- Can students write the four number sentences for each of the fact families?

OBSERVATIONAL ASSESSMENT RECORD

(A1) Can students collect, organize, graph, and analyze data?

(A2) Can students make and interpret point graphs?

(A3) Can students draw and interpret best-fit lines?

(A4) Can students use patterns in data tables and graphs to make predictions?

(A5) Can students measure volume by displacement?

(A6) Can students solve open-response problems and communicate solution strategies?

(A7) Do students demonstrate fluency with the multiplication facts?

(A8) Can students write the four number sentences for each of the fact families?

(A9) _____

Name	A1	A2	A3	A4	A5	A6	A7	A8	A9	Comments
1.										
2.										
3.										
4.										
5.										
6.										
7.										
8.										
9.										
10.										
11.										
12.										
13.										

Name	A1	A2	A3	A4	A5	A6	A7	A8	A9	Comments
14.										
15.										
16.										
17.										
18.										
19.										
20.										
21.										
22.										
23.										
24.										
25.										
26.										
27.										
28.										
29.										
30.										
31.										
32.										

Daily Practice and Problems

Measuring Up: An Assessment Unit

Two Daily Practice and Problems (DPP) items are included for each non-optional class session listed in the Unit Outline. The first item is always a Bit and the second is either a Task or a Challenge. Refer to the Daily Practice and Problems and Home Practice Guide in the *Teacher Implementation Guide* for further information on the DPP. A Scope and Sequence Chart for the DPP can be found in the Scope and Sequence & the NCTM *Principles and Standards* section of the *Teacher Implementation Guide*.

A DPP Menu for Unit 8

Eight icons designate the subject matter of the DPP items. Each DPP item falls into one or more of the categories listed below. A brief menu of the DPP items included in Unit 8 follows.

N Number Sense	**⊞** Computation	**◷** Time	**⬡** Geometry
A–D, F, G, I, J, L, O, S, T, V	B, F, I, N, O, Q, R	P, R	H
⁵ₓ⁷ Math Facts	**$** Money	**♫♫** Measurement	**◩** Data
A, E–G, I, M, S, U, V	Q, R	H, J–L	C, D

The Multiplication and Division Facts

By the end of fourth grade, students in *Math Trailblazers* are expected to demonstrate fluency with all the multiplication and division facts. This unit completes the first phase of the systematic, strategies-based approach to the study of these facts in fourth grade. Students review all five groups of multiplication facts: fives and tens, twos and threes, square numbers, nines, and the last six facts. Their fluency will be assessed with the *Multiplication Facts Inventory Test* given in DPP Bit U in Lesson 8 of this unit.

At the same time that students have been reviewing their multiplication facts, they have been studying the division facts using fact families. In Lesson 8, as they complete their review of the multiplication facts, they will start to focus on the division facts. They will begin a *Division Facts I Know* chart and will learn how to use the *Triangle Flash Cards* to practice the division facts. Practice of the division facts through the DPP and the *Triangle Flash Cards* will continue throughout Units 9–16. Students' fluency with the division facts will be assessed with another inventory test in Unit 16.

To help students prepare for the *Multiplication Facts Inventory Test* in Lesson 8, encourage them to study the multiplication facts at home by using the *Triangle Flash Cards*. Students should study the facts in small groups of 8–10 facts with an emphasis on those facts that have not yet been circled on their *Multiplication Facts I Know* charts. Two copies of a *Triangle Flash Cards Master* appear in the *Discovery Assignment Book* following the Home Practice for this unit. Students who do not have all of their *Triangle Flash Cards,* which were distributed in Units 3–7 in the *Discovery Assignment Book,* may use the masters to make cards for those facts they still need to practice. New copies of the *Triangle Flash Cards* for studying the division facts will be distributed in the *Discovery Assignment Book* in Lesson 8 of this unit and in Units 10–13. Blackline masters for the *Triangle Flash Cards* can be found in the *Unit Resource Guide* Generic Section.

For more information about the distribution and assessment of the math facts, see the TIMS Tutor: *Math Facts* in the *Teacher Implementation Guide*. Also refer to the DPP guide in the *Unit Resource Guides* for Units 3 and 9.

Daily Practice and Problems

Students may solve the items individually, in groups, or as a class. The items may also be assigned for homework.

Student Questions	Teacher Notes

 Mixed-Up Multiplication Table

Complete the table. Look for patterns.

×	2	4	6	8	10
3					
5		20			
7					
9					

TIMS Bit

An inventory test on all of the multiplication facts is given in Bit U in Lesson 8. Tell students when the test will be administered. Part 1 of the Home Practice reminds students to take home their *Triangle Flash Cards* so they can study for the test. Alternatively, students may use the two copies of the *Triangle Flash Cards Master* that follow the Home Practice to make cards for those facts that have not yet been circled on their *Multiplication Facts I Know* charts. Encourage students to study the facts in small groups (8–10 facts at one time) and to focus especially on those facts they do not know or cannot answer quickly.

×	2	4	6	8	10
3	6	12	18	24	30
5	10	20	30	40	50
7	14	28	42	56	70
9	18	36	54	72	90

 More Multiplication

Solve the following problems using paper and pencil or mental math. Estimate to see if your answers are reasonable.

1. A. $26 \times 8 =$ B. $47 \times 6 =$

   C. $87 \times 7 =$ D. $93 \times 5 =$

   E. $63 \times 6 =$ F. $45 \times 8 =$

2. Explain how you solved Question 1A.

TIMS Task

1. A. 208

   B. 282

   C. 609

   D. 465

   E. 378

   F. 360

2. Strategies will vary. Possible strategy: $4 \times 25 = 100$, so $8 \times 25 = 200$. Add $8 \times 1 = 8$ more to get 208.

Median and Mean

Tanya's softball team plays a game once a week. She records the number of runs she scores in a data table.

1. Find the median number of runs Tanya scored in 6 weeks.

2. Find the mean to the nearest whole number.

Week	Number of Runs
1	1
2	0
3	4
4	1
5	1
6	4

TIMS Bit

1. 1 run

2. about 2 runs;
   On the calculator:
   $1 + 0 + 4 + 1 + 1 + 4 = 11$;
   $11 \div 6 = 1.8333333$ or about 2 runs.

 The Rain in Borneo

The average rainfall in Borneo is 160 inches per year. The highest recorded annual rainfall was 225 inches and the lowest was 102 inches. (The wettest state in the mainland U.S. has an average rainfall of 56 inches.)

1. Make up a possible 10-year record of the annual rainfall in Borneo so that the mean rainfall is 160 inches. Keep your values reasonable (102–225 inches).

2. With such a high rainfall, where on Earth would you expect to find Borneo?

TIMS Challenge

1. This exercise builds students' understanding of the concept of average. Their answers will vary, but should average to 160. Note that the sum of the values should add up to 10×160 or 1600 inches. Have them switch papers with a partner and check. It will be interesting for students to see that different sets of numbers can yield the same average.

   Two possible sets of values for ten years: 150", 170", 145", 175", 140", 180", 135", 185", 120", 200" and 145", 150", 102", 146", 180", 218", 175", 154", 170", 160".

2. Borneo is located in the tropics.

Fact Practice

Find the number for *n* that will make each number sentence true. Then write the other number sentences in that fact family.

A. $n \times 7 = 35$ B. $12 \div n = 2$

C. $12 \div n = 4$ D. $8 \times n = 32$

E. $9 \times n = 63$ F. $36 \div n = 6$

G. $40 \div n = 5$ H. $7 \times n = 49$

I. $30 \div n = 6$ J. $n \times 8 = 48$

TIMS Bit

A. $n = 5$
$7 \times 5 = 35$
$35 \div 7 = 5$
$35 \div 5 = 7$

B. $n = 6$
$12 \div 2 = 6$
$2 \times 6 = 12$
$6 \times 2 = 12$

C. $n = 3$
$12 \div 4 = 3$
$4 \times 3 = 12$
$3 \times 4 = 12$

D. $n = 4$
$4 \times 8 = 32$
$32 \div 8 = 4$
$32 \div 4 = 8$

E. $n = 7$
$7 \times 9 = 63$
$63 \div 7 = 9$
$63 \div 9 = 7$

F. $n = 6$
$6 \times 6 = 36$

G. $n = 8$
$40 \div 5 = 8$
$8 \times 5 = 40$
$5 \times 8 = 40$

H. $n = 7$
$49 \div 7 = 7$

I. $n = 5$
$30 \div 6 = 5$
$6 \times 5 = 30$
$5 \times 6 = 30$

J. $n = 6$
$8 \times 6 = 48$
$48 \div 6 = 8$
$48 \div 8 = 6$

Order of Operations

Irma and Jacob are playing *Operation Target.*

1. They recorded these number sentences using 4, 5, 6, and 8. Find the numbers they made.

   A. $4 + 6 + 5 \times 8 =$

   B. $6 \times 8 + 4 \times 5 =$

   C. $6 - 8 \div 4 + 5 =$

   D. $5 + 48 \div 6 =$

2. What is the largest whole number you can make with 4, 5, 6, 8 and one or more of the four operations $(+, -, \times, \div)$?

3. What is the smallest whole number you can make?

TIMS Task

Students were introduced to the game *Operation Target* in Unit 7 Lesson 1. Students may refer back to their *Student Guide* pages. In Lesson 2 of this unit, students played a new version of the game.

1. A. 50

   B. 68

   C. 9

   D. 13

2. $84 \times 65 = 5460$

3. $1; 8 + 4 - 5 - 6$

 Counting Backwards

1. Use your calculator to subtract 4 over and over again from 36.

   Will zero ever be in the display? Why or why not? Try it.

2. Subtract 5 over and over again from 36.

   Will zero ever be in the display? Why or why not? Try it.

3. Subtract 9 over and over again from 36.

   Will zero ever be in the display? Why or why not? Try it.

TIMS Bit

Pressing $36 - 4 = = =$ on a calculator with a constant feature will cause the calculator to repeatedly subtract four.

1. Yes, because $36 \div 4 = 9$. Repeated subtraction is like division. Since the quotient of 36 and 4 is a whole number, 36 is divisible by 4 or 4 is a factor of 36.

2. No, because 36 is not divisible by 5.

3. Yes, because $36 \div 9 = 4$.

Area and Perimeter

1. Sketch the rectangle described below. You may use *Centimeter Grid Paper.*

   The rectangle has a width of 6 cm. The rectangle has a perimeter of 30 cm.

2. What is the area of the rectangle?

1. The rectangle is 6 cm by 9 cm.

2. The area of the rectangle is 54 sq cm.

 Estimation

TIMS Bit

1. Find the following products in your head.

   A. 90 × 40   B. 6000 × 90

   C. 50 × 400   D. 10 × 300

2. Use convenient numbers to estimate the products.

   A. 41 × 70   B. 79 × 82

   C. 2 × 797   D. 81 × 98

1. A. 3600
   B. 540,000
   C. 20,000
   D. 3000

2. A. Answers will vary.
      40 × 70 = 2800
   B. Answers will vary.
      80 × 80 = 6400
   C. Answers will vary.
      2 × 800 = 1600
   D. Answers will vary.
      80 × 100 = 8000

Estimating Volume

1. Estimate the volume of the jar your teacher shows you. Write down your estimate and be ready to share your estimation strategy with the class.

2. After everyone has made his or her estimate, a student from the class will find the volume of the jar using a graduated cylinder.

3. Find 10% of the measured volume of the jar. Is your estimated volume within 10% of the measured volume? Show how you know.

TIMS Task

This item provides practice estimating volume. Choose an odd-shaped jar that has a volume of between 1000 cc and 2000 cc (1 liter and 2 liters) for this activity. Show students 100 cc of water as a benchmark. Discuss students' estimation strategies.

Have students answer Question 3 only if they completed Unit 6 Lesson 5.

 Taking Medicine

When Jerome had a sore throat, his doctor told his parents to give Jerome 1 teaspoon of medicine three times a day for 10 days. One teaspoon is about 5 ml (1 ml = 1 cc).

1. About how many cubic centimeters (cc) of medicine did he take each day?

2. About how many cubic centimeters (cc) did he take in 10 days?

TIMS Bit

1. About 15 cc in one day
2. About 150 cc in 10 days

Estimating Volume Again

1. Estimate the volume of the jar your teacher shows you. Write down your estimate and be ready to share your estimation strategy with the class.

2. After everyone has made his or her estimate, a student from the class will find the volume of the jar using a graduated cylinder.

3. Find 10% of the measured volume of the jar. Is your estimated volume within 10% of the measured volume? Show how you know.

TIMS Task

This item provides practice estimating volume. Choose an odd-shaped jar which has a volume of between 500 cc and 1500 cc for this activity. Show students 100 cc of water as a benchmark. Discuss students' estimation strategies.

Have students answer Question 3 only if they completed Unit 6 Lesson 5.

M **Facts Practice**

Solve the given fact. Then, name the other related fact or facts in the same fact family.

A. $2 \times 8 =$ _____   B. $64 \div 8 =$ _____

C. $24 \div 6 =$ _____   D. $5 \times 9 =$ _____

E. $4 \times 4 =$ _____   F. $63 \div 9 =$ _____

G. $7 \times 3 =$ _____   H. $27 \div 3 =$ _____

TIMS Bit

A. 16; $8 \times 2 = 16$
    $16 \div 8 = 2$
    $16 \div 2 = 8$

B. 8; $8 \times 8 = 64$

C. 4; $24 \div 4 = 6$
    $4 \times 6 = 24$
    $6 \times 4 = 24$

D. 45; $9 \times 5 = 45$
    $45 \div 5 = 9$
    $45 \div 9 = 5$

E. 16; $16 \div 4 = 4$

F. 7; $63 \div 7 = 9$
    $9 \times 7 = 63$
    $7 \times 9 = 63$

G. 21; $3 \times 7 = 21$
    $21 \div 3 = 7$
    $21 \div 7 = 3$

H. 9; $27 \div 9 = 3$
    $3 \times 9 = 27$
    $9 \times 3 = 27$

Arithmetic Review

Solve the following problems using paper and pencil or mental math. Estimate to make sure your answers make sense.

1. A. 3048 B. 6007 C. 9015
   + 253   − 824   +6386

  D. 3005 + 61 + 458 =

  E. 17 + 608 + 3 + 1060 =

  F. 917 − 145 =

2. Explain how you solved Question 1B.

TIMS Task

1. A. 3301

 B. 5183

 C. 15,401

 D. 3524

 E. 1688

 F. 772

2. Strategies will vary. A possible strategy is to count up from 824: 1 + 75 + 100 or 176 to 1000. Count up another 5007 to 6007. 5007 + 176 = 5183.

Languages Spoken at Home

In 2000, about 28,101,052 people over the age of 5 spoke Spanish at home in the United States.

2,022,143 people spoke Chinese.

1,643,838 spoke French.

1,383,442 spoke German.

667,414 spoke Polish.

706,242 spoke Russian.

1,224,241 spoke Tagalog.

1. Write the seven numbers in order from largest to smallest.

2. About how many more people spoke Spanish than French?

3. About how many more people spoke Russian than Polish?

4. About how many more people spoke German than Tagalog?

TIMS Bit

1. 28,101,052; 2,022,143; 1,643,838; 1,383,442; 1,224,241; 706,242; 667,414

2. Estimates will vary. About 26–27 million people

3. Estimates will vary. About 40,000 people

4. Estimates will vary. About 150,000 people

Student Questions	Teacher Notes

P Never too Late!

The school bell rang at 8:25 A.M. Maya arrived 10 minutes early and played with Irma. Irma had already been playing for 20 minutes. When Luis arrived, he joined Irma, but he had to wait about 4 minutes until Maya arrived. Linda arrived 6 minutes before the bell.

1. Tell the order and the time each child arrived at school.

2. How many minutes had gone by from the time the first student arrived until the last student arrived?

TIMS Challenge 🕐

1. Irma—7:55
   Luis—8:11
   Maya—8:15
   Linda—8:19
2. 24 minutes

Q Sharing Money

Five children found $4.00 in the hall at school. The principal said they could share it, if no one claimed it. How much would each child get?

TIMS Bit 💲 ✖️

Each child would get $0.80. Ask students to explain how they solved the problem.

R Payday

Jerome's mother pays him 7¢ for each minute he spends sweeping the floor. He began at 3:45 and finished at 4:17. How much money will he make? Tell the strategies you used to get your answer.

TIMS Task 💲 🕐 ✖️

$2.24

Multiplication Facts

Emma has baked a cake. Here is a square to represent Emma's cake.

A. Show all the ways she can cut the cake if she wants to make 24 equal pieces. Write multiplication number sentences to describe each way.

B. Show all the ways she can cut the cake if she wants to make 30 equal pieces. Write multiplication number sentences to describe each way.

TIMS Bit

For each question discuss which ways of cutting the cake would be best and why. Have students demonstrate on the overhead projector or on the blackboard the various ways the cake can be cut. Have them use their drawings to justify their choices for the best way of cutting the cake. Note that turn-around facts will result in the same pieces.

2 × 12 = 24

A. 1 × 24 = 24, 2 × 12 = 24,
     3 × 8 = 24, 4 × 6 = 24

B. 1 × 30 = 30, 2 × 15 = 30,
     3 × 10 = 30, 5 × 6 = 30

Changing Temperatures

On Monday, when Irma and her father left Chicago, the temperature was 18°F.

1. When they arrived in Michigan Monday afternoon, the temperature was 20 degrees colder than when they left Chicago. What was the temperature in Michigan on Monday?

2. On Tuesday the high temperature in Michigan was -7°F. How many degrees colder was it on Tuesday than on Monday?

3. The temperature on Wednesday went up to 12°F. The windchill, however, made it feel like 10° below zero. How many degrees colder did the wind make the temperature feel on Wednesday?

TIMS Challenge

Use this item with students who completed optional Lesson 6 in Unit 3.

1. -2°F

2. 5 degrees

3. 22 degrees

Student Questions	Teacher Notes

 Multiplication Facts Inventory Test

Students take the *Multiplication Facts Inventory Test.* It contains the multiplication facts from all five groups: 5s and 10s, 2s and 3s, square numbers, 9s, and the last six facts.

We recommend allowing four minutes for this test. Students should have two pens or pencils of different colors ready. During the first four minutes of the test, students write their answers using one color pen or pencil. Encourage students to answer first all the facts they know well and can answer quickly. Then, they should go back and use strategies to solve the rest. After you tell students that four minutes have passed, give them more time to complete the remaining items with the other color pen or pencil.

Students update their *Multiplication Facts I Know* charts using the results of the test.

TIMS Bit

The test can be found at the end of this set of DPP items, following item V. It includes all the basic multiplication facts. Using their results of the test, students circle the facts they know and can answer quickly on their *Multiplication Facts I Know* charts. Then, students discuss strategies for figuring out or remembering any remaining facts that they do not know well. They can record these strategies in their journals.

A second inventory test will be given in Unit 16 for the division facts.

More Facts Practice

Find the number for *n* that will make each number sentence true. Then write the other number sentences in the same fact family.

A. $n \times 7 = 42$

B. $56 \div n = 8$

C. $20 \div n = 5$

D. $9 \times n = 72$

E. $64 \div n = 8$

F. $n \div 4 = 7$

Find the number for *n* that will make each number sentence true.

G. $7 \times n = 2800$

H. $n \times 40 = 2000$

I. $800 \times n = 72{,}000$

J. $n \times 70 = 350$

TIMS Task

A. 6; $7 \times 6 = 42$
   $42 \div 7 = 6$
   $42 \div 6 = 7$

B. 7; $56 \div 8 = 7$
   $7 \times 8 = 56$
   $8 \times 7 = 56$

C. 4; $20 \div 5 = 4$
   $4 \times 5 = 20$
   $5 \times 4 = 20$

D. 8; $8 \times 9 = 72$
   $72 \div 8 = 9$
   $72 \div 9 = 8$

E. 8; $8 \times 8 = 64$

F. 28; $28 \div 7 = 4$
   $4 \times 7 = 28$
   $7 \times 4 = 28$

G. 400

H. 50

I. 90

J. 5

Name _____   Date _____

Multiplication Facts Inventory Test

You will need two pens or pencils of different colors. Use the first color when you begin the test. When your teacher tells you to switch pens, finish the test using the second color.

$\begin{array}{r}9\\ \times 2\\ \hline\end{array}$	$\begin{array}{r}7\\ \times 8\\ \hline\end{array}$	$\begin{array}{r}10\\ \times 4\\ \hline\end{array}$	$\begin{array}{r}5\\ \times 2\\ \hline\end{array}$	$\begin{array}{r}8\\ \times 4\\ \hline\end{array}$
$\begin{array}{r}4\\ \times 2\\ \hline\end{array}$	$\begin{array}{r}6\\ \times 9\\ \hline\end{array}$	$\begin{array}{r}10\\ \times 7\\ \hline\end{array}$	$\begin{array}{r}6\\ \times 5\\ \hline\end{array}$	$\begin{array}{r}8\\ \times 2\\ \hline\end{array}$
$\begin{array}{r}10\\ \times 8\\ \hline\end{array}$	$\begin{array}{r}7\\ \times 7\\ \hline\end{array}$	$\begin{array}{r}5\\ \times 3\\ \hline\end{array}$	$\begin{array}{r}3\\ \times 8\\ \hline\end{array}$	$\begin{array}{r}6\\ \times 10\\ \hline\end{array}$
$\begin{array}{r}9\\ \times 3\\ \hline\end{array}$	$\begin{array}{r}6\\ \times 2\\ \hline\end{array}$	$\begin{array}{r}7\\ \times 9\\ \hline\end{array}$	$\begin{array}{r}10\\ \times 3\\ \hline\end{array}$	$\begin{array}{r}3\\ \times 4\\ \hline\end{array}$
$\begin{array}{r}4\\ \times 5\\ \hline\end{array}$	$\begin{array}{r}3\\ \times 3\\ \hline\end{array}$	$\begin{array}{r}2\\ \times 7\\ \hline\end{array}$	$\begin{array}{r}5\\ \times 5\\ \hline\end{array}$	$\begin{array}{r}9\\ \times 5\\ \hline\end{array}$
$\begin{array}{r}7\\ \times 4\\ \hline\end{array}$	$\begin{array}{r}9\\ \times 9\\ \hline\end{array}$	$\begin{array}{r}6\\ \times 7\\ \hline\end{array}$	$\begin{array}{r}2\\ \times 10\\ \hline\end{array}$	$\begin{array}{r}4\\ \times 6\\ \hline\end{array}$
$\begin{array}{r}2\\ \times 2\\ \hline\end{array}$	$\begin{array}{r}10\\ \times 9\\ \hline\end{array}$	$\begin{array}{r}8\\ \times 8\\ \hline\end{array}$	$\begin{array}{r}4\\ \times 4\\ \hline\end{array}$	$\begin{array}{r}5\\ \times 8\\ \hline\end{array}$
$\begin{array}{r}7\\ \times 5\\ \hline\end{array}$	$\begin{array}{r}10\\ \times 10\\ \hline\end{array}$	$\begin{array}{r}9\\ \times 4\\ \hline\end{array}$	$\begin{array}{r}3\\ \times 6\\ \hline\end{array}$	$\begin{array}{r}6\\ \times 6\\ \hline\end{array}$
$\begin{array}{r}10\\ \times 5\\ \hline\end{array}$	$\begin{array}{r}3\\ \times 7\\ \hline\end{array}$	$\begin{array}{r}9\\ \times 8\\ \hline\end{array}$	$\begin{array}{r}2\\ \times 3\\ \hline\end{array}$	$\begin{array}{r}8\\ \times 6\\ \hline\end{array}$

LESSON GUIDE 1

Volume

This lesson is divided into four parts. In Part 1, students discuss volume using the context of the Aesop's Fable *The Crow and the Pitcher.* If your students have used this curriculum in previous grades, Part 1 can be used as a review. If your students have not had many experiences with measuring volume, Part 1 can be used as an introduction. In Part 2, the procedure for finding the volume of an object by displacement is modeled for students. Students will use this skill in the game in Lesson 2 and the lab in Lesson 3.

Part 3 of the lesson is optional. A third grade activity has been revised and included here to provide students who are new to the curriculum with additional opportunities to measure volume by displacement using a graduated cylinder.

In Part 4 of the lesson, students discuss the appropriate units used to measure volume. They also review the multiplication facts for homework.

Key Content

- Understanding the concept of volume.
- Using appropriate units for measuring volume.
- Measuring volume by displacement.
- Practicing the multiplication facts.

Key Vocabulary

cubic centimeter (cc)   meniscus
cubic foot   milliliters (ml)
cubic units   volume
graduated cylinder   volume by displacement
liters (l)

Daily Practice and Problems: Bit for Lesson 1

A. Mixed-Up Multiplication Table
(URG p. 10)

Complete the table. Look for patterns.

×	2	4	6	8	10
3					
5		20			
7					
9					

DPP Task is on page 32. Suggestions for using the DPPs are on page 32.

Curriculum Sequence

Before This Unit

In both second and third grades, students used graduated cylinders to measure the volume of objects and the volume of containers. They also found the volume of objects by counting cubes. For specific activities on volume in third grade, see Units 16, 18, and 20.

After This Unit

Students will find the volume of prisms in Grade 4 Unit 9.

Materials List

Print Materials for Students

	Math Facts and Daily Practice and Problems	Activity	Homework
Student Books			
Student Guide		*Volume* Pages 216–220	
Discovery Assignment Book		*Estimating and Measuring Volume* Pages 101–102 (optional) and *Triangle Flash Cards Master* Pages 97–99 (optional)	*Estimating and Measuring Volume* Homework Section Pages 103–104 (optional), *Mixed-Up Tables* Pages 105–106, and Home Practice Part 1, Page 93
Teacher Resources			
Facts Resource Guide ⊙	DPP Item 8A Use *Triangle Flash Cards* to review multiplication facts for all groups.		
Unit Resource Guide ⊙	DPP Items A–B Page 10		
Generic Section ⊙		*Three-column Data Table*, 1 per student (optional)	

⊙ *available on Teacher Resource CD*

All Transparency Masters, Blackline Masters, and Assessment Blackline Masters in the Unit Resource Guide are on the Teacher Resource CD.

Supplies for Each Student Pair

centimeter cube (this can be a bit from a set of base-ten pieces)
decimeter cube (this is a pack from a set of base-ten pieces)
ruler
250-cc graduated cylinder, optional
container of water, optional
eyedropper, optional
objects that can be measured in a graduated cylinder such as overhead pens, markers, small rocks, erasers, glue sticks, and lumps of clay, optional
paper towels, optional

Materials for the Teacher

100-cc Graduated Cylinder Scale Transparency Master (Unit Resource Guide) Page 36
250-cc Graduated Cylinder Scale Transparency Master (Unit Resource Guide) Page 37
Reading a Graduated Cylinder Transparency Master (Unit Resource Guide) Page 38
Meniscus Transparency Master (Unit Resource Guide) Page 39
2-liter soda bottle, optional
250-cc graduated cylinder
a small object to measure in a graduated cylinder such as a rock or a lump of clay
eyedropper
container of water

Developing the Activity

Part 1. *The Crow and the Pitcher*

Students begin the activity by reading the story of *The Crow and the Pitcher* in the *Student Guide* and discussing **Questions 1–2.** The crow can raise the level of the water in the pitcher because the rocks displace (or push away) the water. If the rocks have different volumes, they will displace different amounts of water.

Questions 3–5 discuss measuring volume using graduated cylinders. If your students have had previous experiences with volume, they can answer the questions in pairs and report their answers to the class. If your students have had little experience with volume, discuss the questions with the class as a whole. Use the questions and illustrations to review (or introduce) using graduated cylinders to measure volume by displacement.

Help students read the scales on the graduated cylinders in the pictures for **Question 3** and **Question 5** by showing the *100-cc Graduated Cylinder Scale* Transparency Master and the *250-cc Graduated Cylinder Scale* Transparency Master. The 100-cc graduated cylinder shown in the transparency is scaled by ones and the 250 cc is scaled by twos. See Figure 1.

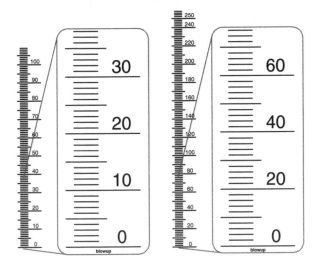

Figure 1: *Scales on a 100-cc graduated cylinder and a 250-cc graduated cylinder*

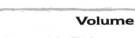

Volume

The Crow and the Pitcher

This is a very old story of a very thirsty crow. The crow, ready to die of thirst, flew with joy to a pitcher which he saw some distance away. When he came to the pitcher, he found water in it, but so near the bottom that he was not able to drink. Then, he tried to knock over the pitcher so he might at least get a little of the water. But, he did not have enough strength for this. At last, seeing some pebbles nearby, he dropped them one by one into the pitcher, so little by little, he raised the water to the very brim and satisfied his thirst.

1. Why did the water in the pitcher rise?
2. Do you think the water in the pitcher rose the same amount each time a pebble was dropped in? Why or why not?

The **volume** of a rock is the amount of space it takes up. The volume of the pitcher is the amount of space inside it.

We measure volume in cubic units. A **cubic centimeter** (cc) is the amount of space taken up by a cube that is one centimeter long on each side.

1 cubic centimeter

What is the total volume of these centimeter connecting cubes?

Student Guide - Page 216

We can also measure the volume of an object using a graduated cylinder. This method is called **measuring volume by displacement** because you find out how much water the object displaces or pushes away.

3. Look carefully at the scale of the graduated cylinder before the cubes are added.
   A. How much water is in this graduated cylinder?
   B. How much water did the cubes displace or push away?

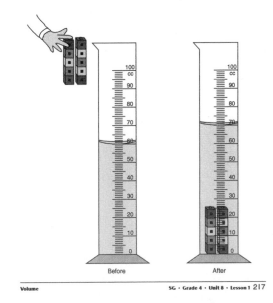

Before   After

Student Guide - Page 217

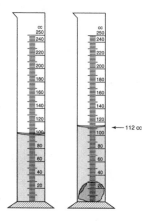

4. We can estimate the volume of a rock by making a model of the rock using centimeter connecting cubes and counting the cubes. Estimate the volume of the rock using the picture of the cubes.

We can find a more exact measure of the volume of the rock by putting it into a graduated cylinder. The volume of the rock is the amount of water it displaces or pushes away.

5. A. Look carefully at the scale of the graduated cylinder before the rock is added. How much water is in the graduated cylinder?

   B. Look at the scale after the rock has been added. What is the volume of the rock?

← 112 cc

218 SG · Grade 4 · Unit 8 · Lesson 1   Volume

Student Guide - Page 218

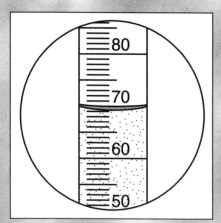

Figure 3: *Meniscus*

TIMS Tip

Objects should be added to graduated cylinders with caution. Some objects will go in, but not come out. Objects should be chosen that fit loosely inside the cylinder. Wooden objects are especially troublesome because they swell when they are wet.

Wooden objects will also float. Objects that float must be pushed under the water with something very thin such as a straightened paper clip, pin, or pencil point.

Part 2. Modeling Measuring Volume by Displacement

As part of Lessons 2 and 3 (*Fill It First* and the assessment lab, *Volume vs. Number*) students will measure the volume of marbles by displacement. Model the procedure for students or have students model one or more of the steps for the rest of the class.

*   Pour a convenient amount of water into a graduated cylinder.

*   Add the last few drops of water with an eyedropper to ensure accuracy.

*   Check the water level before adding the object. Stress that the proper way to read a graduated cylinder is to keep it level on the table and to bend down (if necessary) to read it at eye level. See Figure 2. If students read it from above or below, the angle their eyes make with the graduated cylinder gives a false reading. (*Reading a Graduated Cylinder* Transparency Master illustrates these points.)

Figure 2: *Looking at the graduated cylinder*

*   Tell students that when they try to read the water level, they may see two lines instead of one because water creeps up the sides of the cylinder and forms a **meniscus.** Use the *Meniscus* Transparency Master to show this double line. Instruct students to read the volume from the bottom line. The water level in the graduated cylinder pictured on the transparency and in Figure 3 is 69 cc. (The meniscus may not be as pronounced on plastic graduated cylinders.)

*   Add an object such as a rock or a lump of clay to the cylinder. Show students how to tilt the cylinder and let the object slide slowly into the water so that the water will not splash.

- Read the new level of the water. Remind students to keep the cylinder flat on the table, put their eyes at the level of the water, and to read the bottom line.

- Calculate the volume of the object by subtracting the initial volume of the water from the new reading on the scale. For example, if a 250-cc graduated cylinder has 100 cc of water before an object is added and the water rises to 112 cc as shown in Figure 4, then the volume of the object is 12 cc.

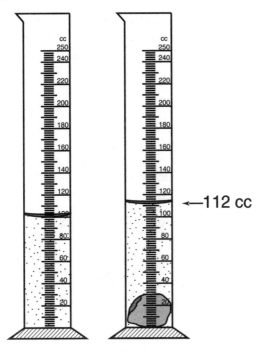

←112 cc

Figure 4: *Measuring volume by displacement*

Part 3. Estimating and Measuring Volume, Optional

This part of the lesson is optional. It is a revised version of an activity in Grade 3 Unit 16 *Volume*. It is included in the *Discovery Assignment Book* for those students who have not studied volume in previous grades. The activity provides practice in estimating the volume of objects using cube models and finding volume by displacement.

This activity works well if students work in pairs to read the directions and answer the questions on the *Estimating and Measuring Volume* Activity Pages in the *Discovery Assignment Book*. *Question 1* asks students to use eight centimeter connecting cubes to build an object that will fit into a graduated cylinder. Each student should understand that the volume of the object is 8 cc. Then, students find the volume of their cubes using a graduated cylinder so that they can see the connection between measuring volume by counting cubes and measuring volume by displacement.

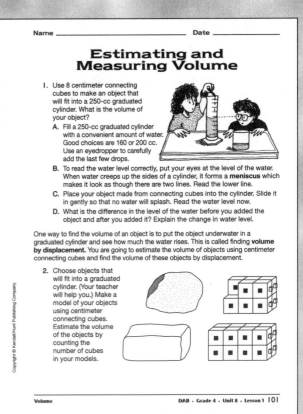

Discovery Assignment Book - Page 101

3. Find the volume of your objects by displacement.

4. Record your results in a table like the one below. Follow the examples.

Volume Data Table

Object	Estimated Volume from Cube Model	Volume by Displacement
Rock	11 cc	12 cc
Marker	14 cc	11 cc
Clay	16 cc	15 cc

5. Frank made a model of a marker using centimeter connecting cubes. By counting the cubes, he estimated that the marker has a volume of 14 cc. When he measured the volume using a graduated cylinder, he found the volume to be 11 cc. Why do you think there is a 3 cc difference?

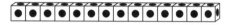

6. Were your estimates close to your measured volumes? Why or why not?

Discovery Assignment Book - Page 102

TIMS Tip

If students completed optional Lesson 5 in Unit 6, they can check to see if their estimates from the cube models are within 10% of the volume of the objects measured by displacement.

Content Note

Milliliters vs. Cubic Centimeters. When we measure objects in *Math Trailblazers,* we often use the cubic centimeter (cc) as our basic unit for measuring volume. As the name implies, a **cubic centimeter** is a cube that has a side length of 1 cm. An object that has a volume of 150 cc takes up the same amount of space as 150 centimeter cubes. When measuring liquid volume using the metric system, the liter is often used as the unit of measure. A cube that is 10 cm on each side has a volume of one liter. Since 10 cm × 10 cm × 10 cm (length × width × height) is 1000 cc, a liter is the same size as 1000 cc. And, $\frac{1}{1000}$ of a liter, a milliliter (ml), has the same volume as 1 cubic centimeter. Since cubic centimeters and milliliters have the same volume, they are often used interchangeably. We have chosen to generally use cubic centimeters instead of milliliters because we believe the image of a cubic centimeter is conceptually easier for young students to visualize than $\frac{1}{1000}$ of a liter. Either unit of measure, however, is correct. Some of the questions in the activities in this unit emphasize the equivalence of these two units of measure.

To complete *Questions 2–6,* students will need three or four small objects that will fit into a 250-cc graduated cylinder. The following objects work well: overhead pens, markers, small rocks, lumps of clay, solid erasers, and glue sticks. Objects that do not work too well are links, spheres, and toys with open spaces. Small toys will work if they are solid or if air pockets are completely enclosed. Students first build models of the objects with centimeter connecting cubes, then estimate the volume of the object by counting the cubes in the model *(Question 2).* After they estimate the volume, students measure the volume of the actual objects by displacement *(Question 3).* They enter both their estimates and measurements in a table as shown in Figure 5 *(Question 4). Question 5* asks why Frank's estimate from his model of a marker is different from his measured volume from the graduated cylinder. Students should see that the marker is slightly thinner than 1 cm and that it tapers off at each end. Frank may have also made an error in his measurement. *Question 6* asks if students' estimates were close to their measured volume.

Volume Data Table

Object	Estimated Volume from Cube Model	Volume by Displacement
Rock	11 cc	12 cc
Marker	14 cc	11 cc
Clay	16 cc	15 cc

Figure 5: *Volume data table*

If students find large discrepancies between their estimates and the measured volume, they may need to rebuild their cube models in order to see the connection between the number of centimeter connecting cubes and volume of water displaced by the actual object.

As homework for this section, assign the Homework section in the *Discovery Assignment Book.* This exercise can also be used to assess how well students can measure volume by displacement.

Part 4. Units of Volume

To complete the lesson, use the remaining discussion questions in the Units of Volume section in the *Student Guide.* As you discuss *Questions 6–8*, which deal with milliliters and liters, use the following discussion prompts. (Each pair of students will need a bit and a pack from a set of base-ten pieces. You will need a 250-cc graduated cylinder and an optional 2-liter soda bottle.)

- *Verify with your rulers that each edge of a bit is 1 centimeter in length. A cube with edges of 1 cm is one cubic centimeter* (1 cc).

- *Measure each edge of a pack.* (Each edge measures 10 cm.)

- *What is the volume of a pack? How many cubic centimeters are in one pack?* (1000 cc)

- *We sometimes measure liquid volume in milliliters. One milliliter is the same as 1 cubic centimeter. This is a 250-cc graduated cylinder. How many milliliters will it hold?* (250 ml)

- *There are 1000 ml in one liter. How many milliliters are there in a 2-liter soda bottle?* (2000 ml)

- *How many cc are in a two-liter soda bottle?* (2000 cc)

- *How can we use the 250-cc graduated cylinder to check the volume of a soda bottle?* (Fill the cylinder with water to the 250-cc line and pour the water into the bottle. Do this eight times. You or your students may want to check the volume of a two-liter bottle this way for the class. However, remind students to fill the graduated cylinder to the 250-cc line carefully using the techniques described in Part 2 Modeling Measuring Volume by Displacement.)

- *If we had an aquarium the size of a pack, each edge would measure 10 centimeters. What is the volume of such an aquarium? How much water would the aquarium hold? (Hint: How many cubic centimeters or bits are in one pack?)* (1 liter, 1000 ml, or 1000 cc)

Question 9 is a challenging problem. It assumes that a 15-cubic-foot refrigerator is shaped so that the maximum number of 12-packs can be stacked inside. Since each 12-pack is half a cubic foot, thirty 12-packs will fit in the refrigerator.

📓 Journal Prompt

How can you measure the volume of a rock which is too large to fit inside a graduated cylinder?

Units of Volume

We can find the volume of a pitcher using a graduated cylinder, too. We sometimes measure liquid volume in **milliliters (ml)** or **liters (l)**.

One milliliter is the same as one cubic centimeter.

1 cc = 1 ml

One liter is 1000 milliliters.

Jackie put water in a graduated cylinder until it reached the 250-cc mark. She emptied the cylinder into a pitcher. She did this four times until the pitcher was full.

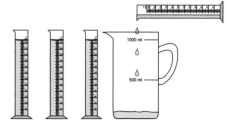

6. What is the volume of the pitcher? Give your answer in cubic centimeters.

7. How many milliliters does the pitcher hold?

8. Give the volume of the pitcher in liters.

Volume   SG · Grade 4 · Unit 8 · Lesson 1   219

Student Guide - Page 219

---

9. A cubic foot is the amount of space taken up by a cube that is one foot long on each side. The volume of a 12-pack of soda is about half a cubic foot. What is the largest number of 12-packs of soda that will fit into a refrigerator that can hold 15 cubic feet?

220 SG · Grade 4 · Unit 8 · Lesson 1   Volume

Student Guide - Page 220

Daily Practice and Problems:
Task for Lesson 1

B. Task: More Multiplication
(URG p. 10)

Solve the following problems using paper and pencil or mental math. Estimate to see if your answers are reasonable.

1. A. $26 \times 8 =$ B. $47 \times 6 =$

    C. $87 \times 7 =$ D. $93 \times 5 =$

    E. $63 \times 6 =$ F. $45 \times 8 =$

2. Explain how you solved Question 1A.

Suggestions for Teaching the Lesson

Math Facts

- DPP Bit A and the *Mixed-Up Tables* Homework Pages in the *Discovery Assignment Book* provide practice with the multiplication facts.

- Home Practice Part 1 reminds students to study the multiplication facts using flash cards. Students can use the *Triangle Flash Card Master*s in the *Discovery Assignment Book* to make flash cards for the facts that are not yet circled on their *Multiplication Facts I Know* charts.

Homework and Practice

- Assign the Homework section on the *Estimating and Measuring Volume* Homework Pages in the *Discovery Assignment Book* after Part 3 (optional).

- Assign the *Mixed-Up Tables* Homework Pages in the *Discovery Assignment Book*.

- DPP Task B provides practice with multiplication.

Name _____ Date _____

Unit 8: Home Practice

Part 1 *Triangle Flash Cards:* Reviewing All the Facts

Study for the test on all the multiplication facts. Take home your *Triangle Flash Cards* for the 5s and 10s, 2s and 3s, square numbers, 9s, and the last six facts. Study the facts in small groups, about 8–10 facts each night.

Here's how to use the flash cards. Ask a family member to choose one flash card at a time. Your partner should cover the corner containing the highest number. This number will be the answer to a multiplication fact. Multiply the two uncovered numbers.

Separate the used cards into three piles: those facts you know and can answer quickly, those that you can figure out with a strategy, and those that you need to learn. Practice the last two piles again. Remember to concentrate on one small group of facts each night—about 8 to 10 facts. Also, remember to study only those facts you cannot answer correctly and quickly.

If you do not have your flash cards, create new ones for those facts that are not yet circled on your *Multiplication Facts I Know* chart. To create your flash cards, use the *Triangle Flash Cards Masters* that follow the Home Practice.

Your teacher will tell you when the test on all the multiplication facts will be.

Part 2 Number Relationships

1. A. Is 51 prime? Tell how you know.

   B. Is 53 prime? Tell how you know.

   C. Is 55 prime? Tell how you know.

2. A. Is 6 a factor of 96? How can you tell?

   B. Is 6 a factor of 116? How can you tell?

3. Make a factor tree to find the prime factors of 54.

MEASURING UP: AN ASSESSMENT UNIT   DAB · Grade 4 · Unit 8   93

Discovery Assignment Book - Page 93

Name _____ Date _____

Triangle Flash Cards Master

- Make a flash card for each fact that is not circled on your *Multiplication Facts I Know* chart. Write the product in the shaded corner of each triangle. Write the factors in the other two corners. Then, cut out the flash cards.
- To quiz you on a multiplication fact, your partner covers the shaded number. Multiply the two uncovered numbers.
- Practice the last two piles again. Then, make a list of the facts you need to practice at home.
- Repeat the directions for your partner.

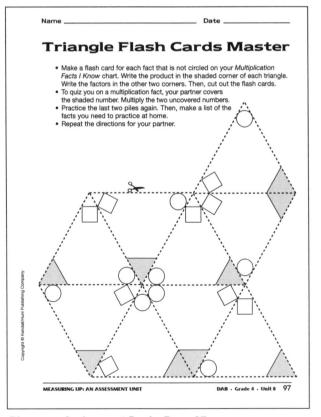

MEASURING UP: AN ASSESSMENT UNIT   DAB · Grade 4 · Unit 8   97

Discovery Assignment Book - Page 97

Assessment

Use the *Estimating and Measuring Volume*
Homework Pages in the *Discovery Assignment Book*
to assess how well students are able to read the
scales on a graduated cylinder.

Literature Connection

• *Aesop's Fables,* as compiled and illustrated by
  Jerry Pinkney, is a collection that includes *The
  Crow and the Pitcher.* The fable as it appears in
  the *Student Guide* is a retelling of the ancient
  story. There are many versions of this story with
  different morals. For example, some versions
  end with "Necessity is the mother of invention,"
  while others conclude with admonishments such
  as "Skill and patience will succeed where force
  fails." Ask students to relate the story to problem
  solving: *How did the crow solve the problem?
  How many strategies did he try? Did he give
  up easily?*

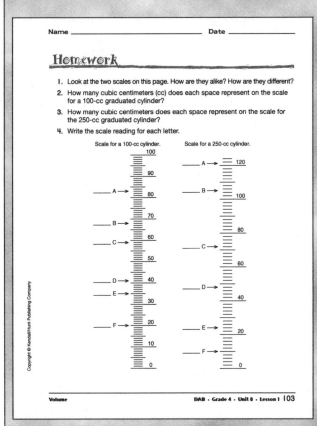

Discovery Assignment Book - Page 103

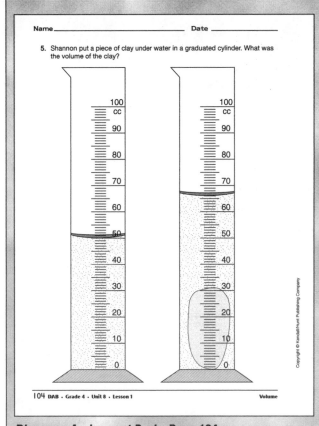

Discovery Assignment Book - Page 104

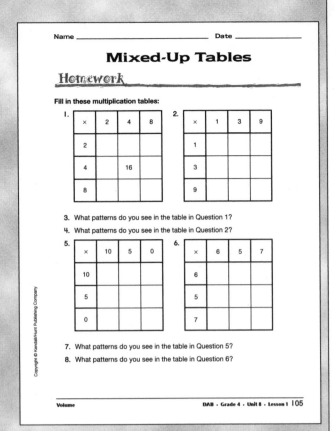

Discovery Assignment Book - Page 105

Name _____ Date _____

Mixed-Up Tables

Homework

Fill in these multiplication tables:

1.

×	2	4	8
2			
4		16	
8			

2.

×	1	3	9
1			
3			
9			

3. What patterns do you see in the table in Question 1?

4. What patterns do you see in the table in Question 2?

5.

×	10	5	0
10			
5			
0			

6.

×	6	5	7
6			
5			
7			

7. What patterns do you see in the table in Question 5?

8. What patterns do you see in the table in Question 6?

Volume   DAB · Grade 4 · Unit 8 · Lesson 1 105

Discovery Assignment Book - Page 106

Name _____ Date _____

9.

×	8	6	4
8			
6			
4			

10.

×	8	6	3
8			
6			
3			

11.

×	2	5	8
9			
4			
7			

12.

×	7	6	4
3			
9			
10			

Fill in these division tables. Divide the large number across the top by the small number on the side.

13.

	Dividend		
÷	24	30	36
2			18
3		10	
6			

(Divisor)

14.

	Dividend		
÷	16	32	40
2			
4			
8			

(Divisor)

106 DAB · Grade 4 · Unit 8 · Lesson 1   Volume

AT A GLANCE

Math Facts and Daily Practice and Problems

DPP Bit A provides practice with multiplication facts. DPP Task B is an exercise in multiplication.

Part 1. *The Crow and the Pitcher*

1. Read Aesop's Fable *The Crow and the Pitcher* in the *Student Guide.*

2. Discuss **Questions 1–2** on the *Volume* Activity Pages in the *Student Guide* concerning volume.

3. Discuss measuring volume by displacement using **Questions 3–5.** Use the *100-cc Graduated Cylinder Scale* and *250-cc Graduated Cylinder Scale* Transparency Masters as part of the discussion.

Part 2. Modeling Measuring Volume by Displacement

Model using a graduated cylinder to measure the volume of an object by displacement. Use the *Meniscus* and *Reading a Graduated Cylinder* Transparency Masters as part of the discussion.

AT A GLANCE

Part 3. Estimating and Measuring Volume, Optional

1. Following the directions on the *Estimating and Measuring Volume* Activity Pages in the *Discovery Assignment Book,* students build an object with eight centimeter connecting cubes.

2. Students find the volume of the eight cubes, carefully following the procedures for measuring volume by displacement.

3. Students build models of real objects out of centimeter connecting cubes. The objects must fit inside a graduated cylinder. They estimate the volume of the objects by counting cubic centimeters.

4. Students measure the volume of the actual objects using a graduated cylinder. They record the volume of each in a table. Then, students compare their estimates to the actual volume of each object.

Part 4. Units of Volume

1. Use prompts in the Lesson Guide to lead a class discussion on units of volume. Students will need one bit, one pack, and a ruler. You will need a 250-cc graduated cylinder and a 2-liter soda bottle.

2. Discuss milliliters and liters using *Questions 6–9* in the *Student Guide* and prompts in the Lesson Guide.

Homework

1. Assign Part 1 of the Home Practice and the *Mixed-Up Tables* Homework Pages in the *Discovery Assignment Book* as homework.

2. Assign the *Estimating and Measuring Volume* Homework Pages in the *Discovery Assignment Book* after Part 3 (optional).

Assessment

Use the *Estimating and Measuring Volume* Homework Pages in the *Discovery Assignment Book* to determine how well students are able to read a graduated cylinder.

Notes:

100-cc Graduated
Cylinder Scale

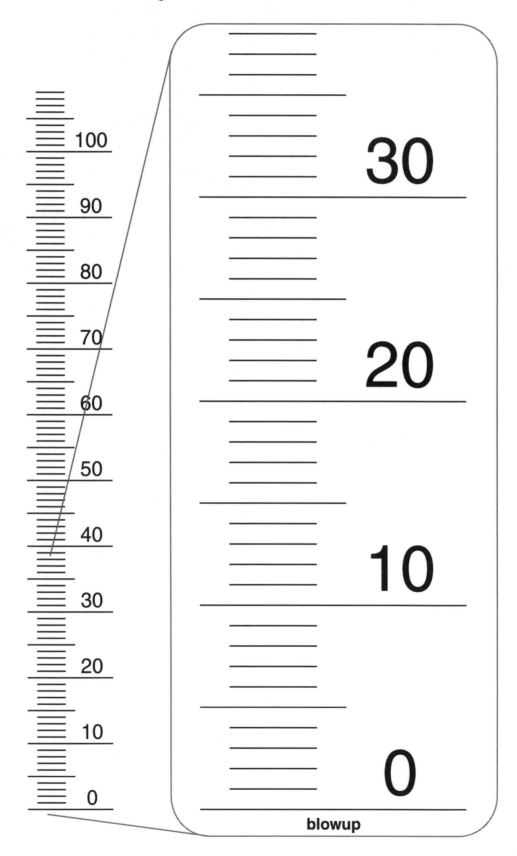

100
90
80
70
60
50
40
30
20
10
0

30

20

10

0

blowup

Transparency Master

250-cc Graduated Cylinder Scale

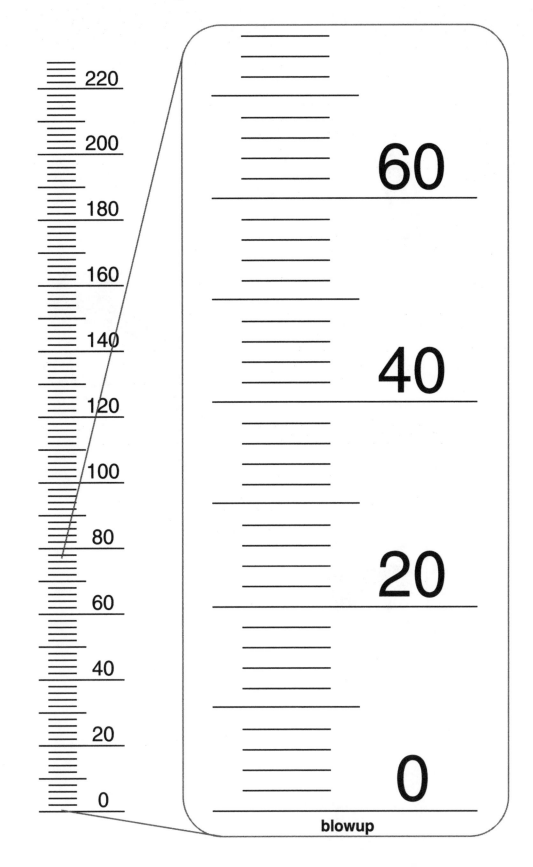

220
200
180
160
140
120
100
80
60
40
20
0

60

40

20

0

blowup

Reading a Graduated Cylinder

Which student is reading the graduated cylinder correctly? Explain.

A

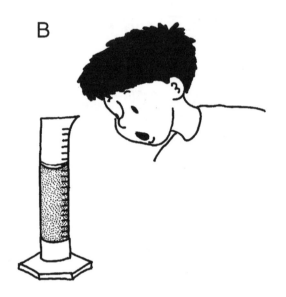

B

C

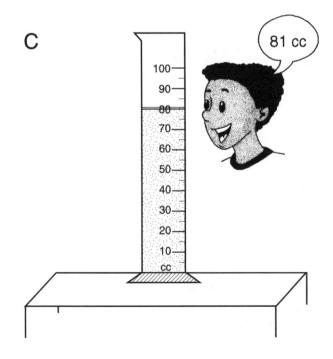

81 cc

Transparency Master

Meniscus

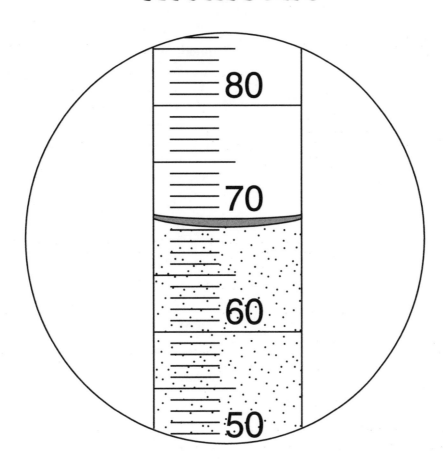

Student Guide

Questions 1–9 (SG pp. 216–220)

1. *As the crow added pebbles to the pitcher, the water in the pitcher was displaced or pushed away by the pebbles, so the water level rose.

2. *No, each pebble took up different amounts of volume, so the water level rose different amounts each time.

3. **A.** 60 cc
   B. 10 cc

4. 11 cc

5. **A.** 100 cc
   B. 12 cc

6. 1000 cc

7. 1000 ml

8. 1 liter

9. *thirty 12-packs

Discovery Assignment Book

Estimating and Measuring Volume (DAB pp. 101–102)

Questions 1–6

1. **D.** *8 cc; The cubes displaced or pushed away 8 cc of water, so the water level went up.

2.–4. *Estimates and volumes will vary based on models made.

5. *Answers will vary. The marker is slightly thinner than one cm and the marker tapers off at the ends. There may also be measurement error.

6. *Answers will vary.

Homework (DAB pp. 103–104)

Questions 1–5

1. Answers will vary. Students may notice that each scale goes up to about 100 and that they both start at zero. On the 100-cc scale, the multiples of 10 are written on the scale. On the 250-cc scale, the multiples of 20 are written on the scale.

2. 1 cc

3. 2 cc

4. 100 cc cylinder: A=83 cc, B=68 cc, C=59 cc, D=41 cc, E=35 cc, F=20 cc

   250 cc cylinder: A=121 cc, B=105 cc, C=72 cc, D=48 cc, E=24 cc, F=10 cc

5. 16 cc

Mixed-Up Tables

Homework (DAB pp. 105–106)

Questions 1–14

1.

×	2	4	8
2	4	8	16
4	8	16	32
8	16	32	64

2.

×	1	3	9
1	1	3	9
3	3	9	27
9	9	27	81

*Answers and/or discussion are included in the Lesson Guide.
**Answers for all the Home Practice in the *Discovery Assignment Book* are at the end of the unit.

3. Answers will vary. Students might see that all the numbers are even, that the numbers double as they go across the rows and down the columns, or that the numbers are the same on the right-to-left, top-to-bottom, diagonals.

4. Answers will vary. Students might see that all the numbers are odd, that the numbers are multiples of three, or that the numbers are the same on the right-to-left, top-to-bottom, diagonals.

5.

×	10	5	0
10	100	50	0
5	50	25	0
0	0	0	0

6.

×	6	5	7
6	36	30	42
5	30	25	35
7	42	35	49

7. Answers will vary. Any number times 0 is 0.

8. Answers will vary. Students might see that there is a pattern in each diagonal. The numbers on the upper left to lower right center diagonal are square numbers.

9.

×	8	6	4
8	64	48	32
6	48	36	24
4	32	24	16

10.

×	8	6	3
8	64	48	24
6	48	36	18
3	24	18	9

11.

×	2	5	8
9	18	45	72
4	8	20	32
7	14	35	56

12.

×	7	6	4
3	21	18	12
9	63	54	36
10	70	60	40

13.

÷	24	30	36
2	12	15	18
3	8	10	12
6	4	5	6

14.

÷	16	32	40
2	8	16	20
4	4	8	10
8	2	4	5

*Answers and/or discussion are included in the Lesson Guide.

**Answers for all the Home Practice in the *Discovery Assignment Book* are at the end of the unit.

C. Median and Mean (URG p. 11)

Tanya's softball team plays a game once a week. She records the number of runs she scores in a data table.

1. Find the median number of runs Tanya scored in 6 weeks.

2. Find the mean to the nearest whole number.

Week	Number of Runs
1	1
2	0
3	4
4	1
5	1
6	4

DPP Challenge is on page 46. Suggestions for using the DPPs are on page 46.

LESSON GUIDE 2
Fill It First

Estimated Class Sessions: 1

In this game, teams of students compete against each other to predict the volume of all the marbles in a graduated cylinder as one to four marbles are added to their cylinders. The winner is the team with the highest score after each team has added a total of 20 cc of marbles.

This game prepares students for the assessment lab in Lesson 3 *Volume vs. Number.* It provides practice for students in measuring volume by displacement and also provides the context for the data collection and the predictions students will make in the lab.

For homework, students review the order of operations and play a new version of the game *Operation Target.*

Key Content

- Reporting a volume measurement using a number and a unit.
- Measuring volume by displacement.
- Estimating volume.
- Using the order of operations.

Materials List

Print Materials for Students

		Math Facts and Daily Practice and Problems	Game	Homework
Student Books	**Student Guide**		*Fill It First* Pages 221–222	*Fill It First* Homework Section Pages 223–224
	Discovery Assignment Book		*Spinner 1–4* Page 107	
Teacher Resources	**Unit Resource Guide**	DPP Items C–D Page 11 ⊙		
	Generic Section ⊙		*Three-column Data Table,* 1 per student (optional)	

⊙ *available on Teacher Resource CD*

All Transparency Masters, Blackline Masters, and Assessment Blackline Masters in the Unit Resource Guide are on the Teacher Resource CD.

Supplies for Each Student Pair

100-cc graduated cylinder
12 marbles in a container
container of water
eyedropper
paper towels

Supplies for Each Group of 4 Students

clear plastic spinner, or a pencil and paper clip to use as a spinner, or a number cube

Materials for the Teacher

Observational Assessment Record (Unit Resource Guide, Pages 7–8 and Teacher Resource CD)

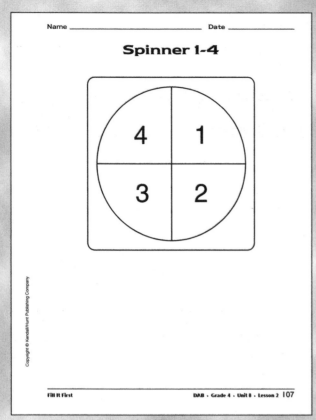

Discovery Assignment Book - Page 107

Student Guide - Page 221

Before the Game

To play the game, each group of four students needs a clear plastic spinner to cover their copy of the *Spinner 1–4* Game Page. If you do not have clear plastic spinners, you can use pencils and paper clips. See Unit 4 Lesson 3 for instructions on making spinners.

Students can also use a number cube. Use only the numbers 1–4 on the cube for this game. If students roll a 5 or a 6 on the number cube, they should roll again.

Developing the Game

Read the directions on the *Fill It First* Game Pages in the *Student Guide*.

Each team fills their graduated cylinder to the 50-cc mark, using an eyedropper for accuracy. The first team spins to determine the number of marbles (one, two, three, or four) to put into their graduated cylinder. Before actually adding the marbles, team members predict the total volume of all the marbles in their cylinder after the marbles are added. Then, they carefully roll their marbles into the cylinder. If the prediction is correct, the team scores one point for each marble added. A bonus of three points is awarded to the first team that has a total of 20 cc of marbles in their cylinder. The team with the highest score wins.

Here are some additional suggestions:

1. Agree on the rules as to what constitutes a correct prediction. Students should discuss how close their prediction must be to the measured volume after adding the marbles. A prediction within 1 cc of the result is a reasonable choice, but this can be their decision.

2. Different starting amounts of water can be used; however, they should be tested first. If an amount is too low, the marbles will pile up above the water line before 20 cc of marbles can be added.

3. Other sizes of graduated cylinders can be used. Starting with 200 cc of water in a 250-cc graduated cylinder will work. If a larger cylinder is used, the total volume of marbles needed to end the game can be more than 20 cc.

4. For classrooms with a shortage of graduated cylinders, a variation of the game can be played in which both teams put their marbles into the same cylinder. Scoring remains the same and the game ends when a total of 20 cc of marbles is added to the cylinder by both teams. The team that adds the last marbles gets the bonus.

Note that some marbles may not be of uniform size. Therefore, the increments may not be exact for students to make their predictions. This only adds challenge to the game.

Journal Prompt

What strategies did you use to predict the volume of marbles in the graduated cylinder while you were playing the game?

---

2. Each team makes a score sheet like the one shown here:

Fill It First Score Sheet

Predicted Volume in cc	Actual Volume in cc	Points

3. Team 1 spins the spinner to find out whether to add one, two, three, or four marbles to the water in their graduated cylinder.

4. Before adding the marbles, Team 1 predicts the volume of the marbles and records the prediction on the score sheet.

5. Team 1 carefully slides the marble(s) into the water and calculates the volume of the marbles. If their prediction is correct, the team scores one point for each marble added. Both teams must agree on the actual volume of the marbles. Then, Team 2 takes a turn.

6. When it is Team 1's turn again, they spin to find the number of marbles they will add to their cylinder. Before adding the marbles, team members predict the **total** volume of all the marbles in the cylinder after the new marbles are added. Then, they slide the marbles into the cylinder. If they predicted correctly, they earn a point for each new marble added.

7. The first team to have a total of 20 cc of marbles in their cylinder scores an extra three points. The team then waits for the other team to have a total of 20 cc of marbles.

8. The team with the highest score wins.

Fill It First

Student Guide - Page 222

D. Challenge: The Rain in Borneo (URG p. 11)

The average rainfall in Borneo is 160 inches per year. The highest recorded annual rainfall was 225 inches and the lowest was 102 inches. (The wettest state in the mainland U.S. has an average rainfall of 56 inches.)

1. Make up a possible 10-year record of the annual rainfall in Borneo so that the mean rainfall is 160 inches. Keep your values reasonable (102–225 inches).

2. With such a high rainfall, where on Earth would you expect to find Borneo?

Suggestions for Teaching the Lesson

Homework and Practice

- Assign the Order of Operations Review in the Homework section in the *Student Guide.* Students solve problems and play a new version of the game *Operation Target.* This game provides practice using the correct order of operations and also provides practice with math facts. Note that the last question is a challenge. You may want to make it an optional part of the assignment. Refer students to the activity *Order of Operations* in Unit 7 Lesson 1, if they need to review.

- DPP items C and D provide practice finding and analyzing means and medians.

Assessment

As students play the game, *Fill It First,* assess their skills in measuring volume by displacement. Record this information on the *Observational Assessment Record.*

Homework

Order of Operations Review

Solve the problems. Remember to use the correct order of operations. First, do all the multiplications and divisions, working from left to right. Then, do all the additions and subtractions, working from left to right.

If you are using a calculator from home, check to see if it follows the correct order of operations. Try the first example. If the answer in the display is 10, then the calculator follows the order of operations. If the calculator gives an answer of 1, then it does not follow the order of operations.

Here are two examples:

    A. $6 \times 2 - 8 \div 4 = ?$ (First, multiply 6 times 2. Also, divide 8 by 4.)
       $12 - 2 = ?$ (Then, subtract 2 from 12.)
       $12 - 2 = 10$

    B. $8 + 4 \times 6 - 1 = ?$ (First, multiply: $4 \times 6 = 24$.)
       $8 + 24 - 1 = ?$ (Then, add and subtract from left to right.)
       $32 - 1 = 31$

I. $6 \times 4 \div 8 + 1 = ?$ 2. $6 \times 4 \div 1 + 8 = ?$

3. $6 \times 4 \div 8 \times 1 = ?$ 4. $8 + 16 \div 4 = ?$

***Student Guide* - Page 223**

Operation Target

Operation Target is a game that can be played many ways. One set of rules for the game is in Unit 7 Lesson 1. Here is another way to play:

- Use the four digits 1, 4, 6, and 8 and four operations (+, −, ×, and ÷).
- You must use each of the four digits exactly once.
- You can use each operation more than once or not at all.
- You can make two-digit numbers by putting two digits together. For example, you can use the numbers 14 or 68.
- No operation should give you a fraction, a decimal, or a negative number.

5. Here is a way to make the number 1:
    $4 - 18 \div 6 = ?$ (First, divide: $18 \div 6 = 3$)
    $4 - 3 = 1$ (Then, subtract 3 from 4.)

    Find another way to make the number 1 following the new rules.

6. Make at least five numbers using these rules.

7. What is the largest number you can make?

8. What is the smallest number you can make?

Challenge: Make all the numbers from 0 to 9.

***Student Guide* - Page 224**

AT A GLANCE

Math Facts and Daily Practice and Problems

DPP items C and D provide practice using medians and means.

Developing the Game

1. Read and discuss the rules for *Fill It First* in the *Student Guide*.
2. Each team fills a 100-cc graduated cylinder with 50 cc of water.
3. Students play the game.

Homework

Assign the Order of Operations Review in the Homework section in the *Student Guide*.

Assessment

As students play the *Fill It First* game, assess their skills in measuring volume by displacement. Record your observations on the *Observational Assessment Record*.

Notes:

Student Guide

Homework (SG pp. 223–224)

Questions 1–8

1. 4
2. 32
3. 3
4. 12
5. Answers will vary. One possible solution: $6 + 4 - 8 - 1 = 1$.
6. Answers will vary. Three examples are: $84 \div 6 \times 1 = 14$; $1 + 68 \div 4 = 18$; $46 + 81 = 127$
7. 5184; $81 \times 64 = 5184$

8. $0; 14 - 8 - 6 = 0$

Challenge: A possible number sentence for each number between 0–9 is:

$$14 - 8 - 6 = 0$$
$$6 + 4 - 8 - 1 = 1$$
$$6 \times 1 + 4 - 8 = 2$$
$$4 + 6 + 1 - 8 = 3$$
$$6 - 8 \div 4 \div 1 = 4$$
$$8 + 4 - 6 - 1 = 5$$
$$8 + 4 - 6 \times 1 = 6$$
$$8 \div 4 + 6 - 1 = 7$$
$$8 \div 4 + 6 \div 1 = 8$$
$$8 + 6 - 4 - 1 = 9$$

*Answers and/or discussion are included in the Lesson Guide.
**Answers for all the Home Practice in the *Discovery Assignment Book* are at the end of the unit.

E. Fact Practice (URG p. 12)

Find the number for *n* that will make each number sentence true. Then write the other number sentences in that fact family.

A. $n \times 7 = 35$	B. $12 \div n = 2$
C. $12 \div n = 4$	D. $8 \times n = 32$
E. $9 \times n = 63$	F. $36 \div n = 6$
G. $40 \div n = 5$	H. $7 \times n = 49$
I. $30 \div n = 6$	J. $n \times 8 = 48$

G. Counting Backwards (URG p. 13)

1. Use your calculator to subtract 4 over and over again from 36.

   Will zero ever be in the display? Why or why not? Try it.

2. Subtract 5 over and over again from 36.

   Will zero ever be in the display? Why or why not? Try it.

3. Subtract 9 over and over again from 36.

   Will zero ever be in the display? Why or why not? Try it.

I. Estimation (URG p. 14)

1. Find the following products in your head.

A. 90×40	B. 6000×90
C. 50×400	D. 10×300

2. Use convenient numbers to estimate the products.

A. 41×70	B. 79×82
C. 2×797	D. 81×98

DPP Tasks and Challenge are on page 53. Suggestions for using the DPPs are on pages 53–55.

LESSON GUIDE

Volume vs. Number

Estimated Class Sessions: 3–4

Students are assessed on their abilities to use the TIMS Laboratory Method to solve problems. They collect, organize, graph, and analyze data on the volume of different numbers of marbles. They look for patterns in the data that will help them predict the volume of a given number of marbles. The game in Lesson 2 *Fill It First* provides the context for the lab. If students can make accurate predictions, they will be more successful at the game.

Key Content

- Measuring volume by displacement.
- Collecting, organizing, graphing, and analyzing data.
- Making and interpreting point graphs.
- Drawing and interpreting best-fit lines.
- Using patterns in tables and graphs to make predictions about data.
- Communicating the solution to a problem.
- Connecting mathematics and science: measuring volume.
- Using numerical variables.

Curriculum Sequence

Before This Unit

TIMS Laboratory Method. Students used the TIMS Laboratory Method to collect, organize, graph, and analyze data in Units 1, 2, and 5 of fourth grade.

Best-Fit Lines. Students used best-fit lines to make predictions in Unit 5.

Using 10% as a Benchmark. Optional Lesson 5 in Unit 6 developed skills so that students can use 10% as a benchmark for deciding if a prediction is "close enough."

After This Unit

Students will continue to use skills addressed in this lab as they work on more experiments in Units 10, 15, and 16. The lab in Unit 16 is also an assessment lab, so students' work on the assessment lab *Perimeter vs. Length* in Unit 2 and *Volume vs. Number* in this unit can be compared to their work at the end of the year.

Materials List

Print Materials for Students

		Math Facts and Daily Practice and Problems	Assessment Lab	Homework
Student Books	**Student Guide**		*Volume vs. Number* Pages 225–229 and Student Rubic: *Solving* Appendix B and Inside Back Cover 	
	Discovery Assignment Book			*Predicting Prices* Pages 109–111 and Home Practice Parts 2 & 3 Pages 93–94
Teacher Resources	**Facts Resource Guide** 	DPP Items 8E–8G & 8*I*		
	Unit Resource Guide 	DPP Items E–J Pages 12–15		
	Generic Section 		*Two-column Data Table,* 2 per student (optional) and *Centimeter Graph Paper,* 1 per student	

available on Teacher Resource CD

All Transparency Masters, Blackline Masters, and Assessment Blackline Masters in the Unit Resource Guide are on the Teacher Resource CD.

Supplies for Each Student Pair

250-cc graduated cylinder
25 standard-size marbles
10–12 $\frac{3}{4}$-inch plastic spheres or marbles larger than the standard size
container for marbles
container of water
eyedropper
paper towels
rulers

Materials for the Teacher

Poster or transparency of TIMS Student Rubric: *Solving* (Teacher Implementation Guide, Assessment section), optional
Observational Assessment Record (Unit Resource Guide, Pages 7–8 and Teacher Resource CD)

Volume vs. Number

Planning the Experiment

Mrs. Dewey's class is playing the game *Fill It First* using marbles. Frank and Nicholas are on one team and Jackie and Maya are on the other team. Jackie and Maya have been able to predict correctly the volume of the marbles more often than Frank and Nicholas.

"We lost again. They sure are lucky!" said Frank. "Their predictions are right almost every time."

"It may not be luck," said Nicholas. "They may have a way to figure out what the volume will be."

"How do they do it?" asked Frank.

"I don't know," said Nicholas. "Maybe they are following a pattern."

"I sure can't see a pattern on our score sheet. The numbers jump around too much," said Frank. "Before we play again, let's make a table that can help us make better predictions. We can find the volume of different numbers of marbles and look for a pattern that can help us."

Frank and Nicholas's Score Sheet

Predicted Volume in cc	Actual Volume in cc	Points
10 cc	6 cc	0
12 cc	11 cc	3
15 cc	13 cc	0

"Won't that be cheating?" asked Nicholas.

"Not if we figure it out for ourselves," said Frank. "We need to do something. Mrs. Dewey said that the next time we play the game, we are going to use a different-size marble. We'll have to think about the numbers of marbles, volume, and which size of marble we're using. We'll never be able to keep all that straight."

Volume vs. Number   SG · Grade 4 · Unit 8 · Lesson 3 225

Student Guide - Page 225

"Okay. Let's figure something out and ask Mrs. Dewey if we can work on it before we play the game again," said Nicholas. "Whatever we do, we'll have to do two experiments, one for each size of marble."

Here are Frank and Nicholas's data tables:

Small Marbles

N Number of Marbles	V Volume in cc
2	
4	
8	

Large Marbles

N Number of Marbles	V Volume in cc

Mrs. Dewey thought Frank and Nicholas had such a good idea that she encouraged all the teams to design experiments to help them make predictions: "If you use the TIMS Laboratory Method, it will help you organize your thinking."

You are going to do the experiments Mrs. Dewey's class is working on. The results of the experiments should help you make predictions when you play the game *Fill It First*. Here are some things to think about as you plan your experiments:

 Discuss

1. What are the two main variables in the experiments?

2. A. Which of the two main variables is the manipulated variable? Justify your answer.
   B. Which is the responding variable? Justify your answer.
   C. What letters will you use to stand for the two main variables?

3. The boys want to look for patterns in the data to help them make predictions about the volume of the marbles when they know the number of marbles. What important variable should be held fixed in each experiment so that they can do this?

226 SG · Grade 4 · Unit 8 · Lesson 3   Volume vs. Number

Student Guide - Page 226

Before the Lab

Students should play the game *Fill It First* in the previous lesson.

Developing the Lab

Part 1. Introducing the Lab, Identifying the Variables, and Drawing the Picture

The Planning the Experiment section of the *Volume vs. Number* Lab Pages in the *Student Guide* develops the context for the lab. Two students in Mrs. Dewey's class look over their score sheet for the game *Fill It First* and try to find a pattern that will help them improve their performance in the game. They decide to collect data as part of a lab. After reading the section, allow a few minutes for the students to discuss their own results playing the game. Have them make conjectures about their own scores as well as those of the two teams in Mrs. Dewey's class.

The questions at the end of this discussion will help students identify the variables in the two experiments. The two main variables in the experiments are the Number of Marbles and the Volume of the marbles in the graduated cylinder *(Question 1)*. At the beginning of the experiments, students will choose the number of marbles they will add to the cylinder, so the Number of Marbles is the manipulated variable *(Question 2A)*. The Volume of the marbles is the responding variable since students will find the volume during the experiments *(Question 2B)*. To be able to find a relationship between the number and volume of the marbles, the size of marble must be held fixed *(Question 3)*.

Students will actually conduct two experiments: one using small (standard-size marbles) and one using larger spheres. Within each experiment, the number and total volume of the marbles in the graduated cylinders will vary, but the size of the marbles will stay the same.

Question 4 asks students to choose values for the number of marbles that will help them see patterns in their data. In the vignette in the *Student Guide,* the two students decide to find the volume of two, four, and eight marbles. Choosing values for the manipulated variable that double or that are multiples of one another will help students see corresponding patterns in the values of the responding variable. You may need to help students choose values for the two experiments. Do not choose values greater than eight marbles.

After students have read and discussed the Planning the Experiment section, they are ready to begin the Conducting the Experiment section. As usual, the first step in the lab is to draw a picture of the experiment. Figure 6 shows such a picture. Note that the artist showed the technique for measuring volume by displacement and that the variables are clearly labeled.

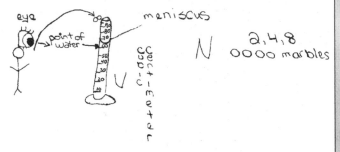

Figure 6: *Student drawing of the experiment* Volume vs. Number

Part 2. Collecting the Data

Before students begin collecting the data, they label the columns of the *Two-column Data Tables* and fill in the left-hand columns with the values they have chosen for the number of marbles. Students should use a 250-cc graduated cylinder for both experiments and choose a convenient amount of water. A good choice is 140 cc. Figure 7 shows sample data for small (standard size) marbles in Experiment 1 and large ($\frac{3}{4}$-inch) spheres in Experiment 2. If you use marbles that are a different size, you may need to adjust the amount of water in the graduated cylinders.

Part 3. Graphing the Data

Students graph the data from both experiments on a single sheet of *Centimeter Graph Paper*. In addition to the points in the data table, they should add a point at (0, 0) since the volume of 0 marbles is 0 cc *(Question 6). Question 7* instructs students to draw best-fit lines through each set of data points.

The graph for this experiment is very similar to the graphs students drew for *Bouncing Ball* in Unit 5. They should be ready to make their graphs with very little assistance from you. If you use marbles that are larger than $\frac{3}{4}$ inch in diameter, your students may need to use a different scale on the vertical axis.

4. A. What values for the number of small marbles did Frank and Nicholas choose?
   B. How will these values help them see patterns?
   C. What values will you choose?

Conducting the Experiment

You will collect and organize data that will help you make predictions about the volume of marbles when you know the number of marbles. You will investigate two sizes of marbles, so you will need to do two experiments.

Make a plan for your experiments. Draw a picture of your plan. Be sure to identify the variables in your picture. Label the main variables with letters.

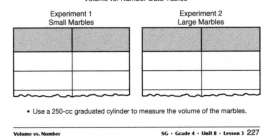

- Label the columns of each of the *Two-column Data Tables* with the variables. Include units where needed.
- Your teacher will help you choose at least three values for the manipulated variable. The largest value will be no more than 8 marbles.

Volume vs. Number Data Tables

Experiment 1 Small Marbles		Experiment 2 Large Marbles	

- Use a 250-cc graduated cylinder to measure the volume of the marbles.

Volume vs. Number   SG · Grade 4 · Unit 8 · Lesson 3 **227**

Student Guide - Page 227

Experiment 1 Small Marbles		Experiment 2 Large Marbles	
N Number of Marbles	*V* Volume (in cc)	*N* Number of Marbles	*V* Volume (in cc)
2	4	2	7
4	7	4	14
8	14	8	29

Figure 7: *Sample data tables*

- Choose a convenient amount of water to use in your cylinder. Use at least 140 cc.
- Collect the data.

Graph

Graph your data on a piece of *Centimeter Graph Paper*.

- Label each axis and write in the units.
- The scale on the horizontal axis should go to 15 or more.
- The scale on the vertical axis should go to 40 or more.

5. Plot your data points for both sizes of marbles on a single piece of graph paper.

6. When the number of marbles equals 0, what is the volume of the marbles? Add this point to your graph for both sets of data.

7. A. If your points for the small marbles lie close to a line, use a ruler to draw a best-fit line.

   B. If your points for the large marbles lie close to a line, use a ruler to draw a best-fit line.

Explore

8. Why does the water level rise when you add marbles to the graduated cylinder?

9. Compare the line for the larger marble to the line for the smaller marble. How are they alike? How are they different?

10. A. Use your graph to estimate the volume of 7 small marbles. Show your work on your graph. Record your estimate.

    B. Did you use interpolation or extrapolation to find your answer?

    C. Check your estimate. Measure the volume of 7 small marbles. Record the volume.

Student Guide - Page 228

D. How close is your estimate to the measured volume? Is it within 1 or 2 cc?

E. If your estimate was not close, you may need to correct your data on your graph before answering any more questions. Your teacher can help you decide.

11. A. Predict the volume of 15 small marbles using your graph. Show how you made your prediction. Record your prediction.

    B. Did you use interpolation or extrapolation to find your answer?

    C. Check your prediction by measuring the volume of 15 small marbles. Record the measured volume.

    D. How close is your prediction to the measured volume? Is it within 3 cc?

12. A. Estimate the volume of 24 small marbles. Explain how you made your prediction and record it.

    B. Check your prediction by measuring the volume of 24 small marbles. Record the measured volume.

    C. How close is your prediction to the measured volume? Is it within 4 cc or 5 cc?

13. Irma and Jessie are playing *Fill It First* with the same large marbles you used. When they add the marbles for their turn, they will have a total of 9 marbles. Help them predict the volume of the 9 marbles. Show how you made your prediction.

14. Irma and Jessie have 150 cc of water in their graduated cylinder. They have added large marbles until the water level is 168 cc. How many large marbles are in the cylinder? Explain how you know.

15. Two students brought marbles from home. Keenya did the experiment with her marbles and Jacob did the experiment with his. They graphed their data on the same graph. Which line (A or B) did Keenya draw? Explain.

Student Guide - Page 229

As you assess the graphs, check for appropriate scales, labels, and titles. Look also for points that have been plotted correctly and lines that "fit" the points. Figure 8 is a graph of the sample data in Figure 7.

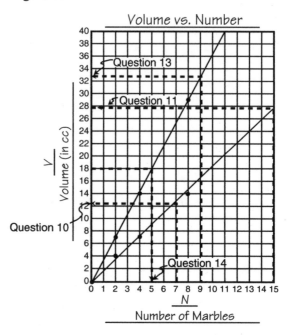

Figure 8: *Graph of sample data for* Volume vs. Number

Part 4. Exploring the Data

The questions are designed to assess students' abilities to make predictions based on data. ***Question 10*** asks students to use their graphs to estimate the volume of seven small marbles and then to check their predictions. If your class completed optional Lesson 5 in Unit 6, have students determine whether their estimates in ***Questions 10, 11, and 12*** are within 10%. If you omitted Lesson 5 in Unit 6, tell students that for ***Question 10,*** their estimates should be within 1 or 2 cc. For ***Question 11,*** the predictions should be within 3 cc. For ***Question 12,*** the predictions should be within 4 or 5 cc. If a group finds that their estimate for ***Question 10*** is not within 1 or 2 cc, they may need to check their data or correct their graph before continuing with the rest of the questions. The dotted lines on the graph in Figure 8 show solutions to ***Questions 10, 11, 13, and 14*** using the data from the tables in Figure 7.

Journal Prompt

Think back to the beginning of the school year. Do you work better in a group now than you did then? Why or why not?

Suggestions for Teaching the Lesson

Math Facts

DPP items E, F, G, and I provide practice with math facts in varying contexts.

Homework and Practice

- Assign the *Predicting Prices* Activity Pages in the *Discovery Assignment Book*. These pages provide practice in looking for patterns in graphs, drawing best-fit lines, and using graphs to make predictions. These pages will help students review for the graphing in the lab and prepare for the *Midyear Test*.

- DPP Challenge H provides a problem that students solve using concepts of area and perimeter.

- Assign the *Review Problems* Activity Pages in the *Student Guide* for Lesson 4. These questions review many concepts and procedures explored in the first seven units. They will help students review for the *Midyear Test*.

- Parts 2 and 3 of the Home Practice may be assigned as homework. Part 2 of the Home Practice reviews primes, factors, and multiples. Part 3 provides computation and mental math practice.

Answers for Parts 2 and 3 of the Home Practice can be found in the Answer Key at the end of this lesson and at the end of this unit.

Assessment

This lab gives you the opportunity to assess students' performance on a task that takes several days to complete. Such a task requires students to use many skills and concepts in context. The following is a list of suggestions for evaluating students' work.

- Use the Assessment section in the *Teacher Implementation Guide* to assist you in scoring students' work in this laboratory investigation. Teachers often assign a given number of points for each part of the lab (picture, data table, graph, and questions) and then grade the students' work accordingly. You may also choose to grade just one part of the lab. Points can be assigned based on the following criteria:

Drawing the Picture:

1. Did the student draw a picture that describes the experiment?

2. Are the variables (Number of Marbles and Volume) shown clearly?

3. Are the variables properly labeled in the picture with N and V?

Name _____ Date _____

Unit 8: Home Practice

Part 1 *Triangle Flash Cards:* Reviewing All the Facts

Study for the test on all the multiplication facts. Take home your *Triangle Flash Cards* for the 5s and 10s, 2s and 3s, square numbers, 9s, and the last six facts. Study the facts in small groups, about 8–10 facts each night.

Here's how to use the flash cards. Ask a family member to choose one flash card at a time. Your partner should cover the corner containing the highest number. This number will be the answer to a multiplication fact. Multiply the two uncovered numbers.

Separate the used cards into three piles: those facts you know and can answer quickly, those that you can figure out with a strategy, and those that you need to learn. Practice the last two piles again. Remember to concentrate on one small group of facts each night—about 8 to 10 facts. Also, remember to study only those facts you cannot answer correctly and quickly.

If you do not have your flash cards, create new ones for those facts that are not yet circled on your *Multiplication Facts I Know* chart. To create your flash cards, use the *Triangle Flash Cards Masters* that follow the Home Practice.

Your teacher will tell you when the test on all the multiplication facts will be.

Part 2 Number Relationships

1. A. Is 51 prime? Tell how you know.

   B. Is 53 prime? Tell how you know.

   C. Is 55 prime? Tell how you know.

2. A. Is 6 a factor of 96? How can you tell?

   B. Is 6 a factor of 116? How can you tell?

3. Make a factor tree to find the prime factors of 54.

MEASURING UP: AN ASSESSMENT UNIT   DAB · Grade 4 · Unit 8   **93**

Discovery Assignment Book - Page 93

Name _____ Date _____

Part 3 Performing Operations

1. Solve the following problems using paper and pencil or mental math.

   A. 459 + 769 =   B. 1078 + 5498 =   C. 7089 − 2793 =

   D. 38 × 5 =   E. 700 × 90 =   F. 44 × 6 =

2. Shannon's dad is taking two night courses at a community college. Each course costs $86. Each of his two textbooks costs $45. How much does Shannon's dad have to pay to go to school?

3. In the 2001–2002 basketball season, Shaquille O'Neal of the Los Angeles Lakers averaged 27 points a game. If Shaquille played in 67 games, about how many points did he score?

4. In the 1992 presidential election, Bill Clinton received 44,908,254 votes. George Bush received 39,102,343 votes. About how many more votes did President Clinton get than Bush?

5. It takes the Earth about 365 days to revolve around the sun. Mercury's revolution around the sun takes 277 fewer days than the Earth's. How many days does it take Mercury to revolve around the sun?

94 DAB · Grade 4 · Unit 8   MEASURING UP: AN ASSESSMENT UNIT

Discovery Assignment Book - Page 94

Suggestions for Teaching the Lesson (*continued*)

Collecting and Recording the Data:

1. Are the columns in the data tables appropriately labeled (*N,* Number of Marbles and *V,* Volume)?

2. Is each data table labeled with the appropriate size of marble?

3. Are the units (cc) included in the data table?

Graphing the Data:

1. Does the graph have a title?

2. Are the axes labeled and scaled correctly?

3. Is Number of Marbles on the horizontal axis and Volume in cc on the vertical axis?

4. Are the points plotted correctly?

5. Did the student use a ruler to draw the best-fit lines?

6. Do the lines fit the points?

7. Did the student show work on his or her graph to solve problems?

Interpreting the Data and Solving the Problems:

1. Are the answers for the problems correct based upon the student's data?

2. Did the student write full explanations?

- Use the *Observational Assessment Record* to note students' skills in measuring volume by displacement.

- *Question 12* asks students to predict the volume of 24 small marbles. They will probably not be able to read the answer directly from the graph, so students will need to use other problem-solving strategies to find the solution. Review the Student Rubric: *Solving* with the class and then use the Solving dimension of the *TIMS Multidimensional Rubric* to score the students' responses to this question.

- Students should include this lab in their collection folders. In Lesson 7 *Midyear Experiment and Portfolio Review,* you and your students may choose to transfer this lab from the collection folders to students' portfolios. Both you and the students will be able to look for growth in many areas of mathematics by comparing this lab to other labs completed earlier in the year. When more labs are added to the portfolio in the future, you can make further comparisons.

Extension

- When students have completed *Questions 1–11*, they can play *Fill It First* again. If they use their graphs and data tables from the lab, they should be able to make more accurate predictions than when they played the first time.

- DPP Task J asks students to estimate the volume of a mystery jar and check their estimates.

Software Connection

Students can organize and graph their data using a spreadsheet or graphing program.

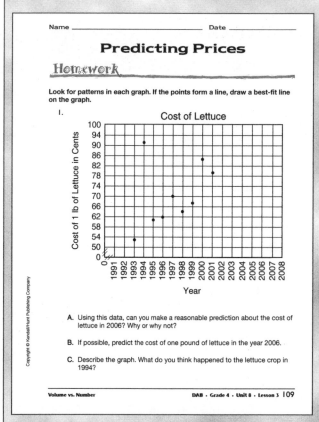

Discovery Assignment Book - Page 109

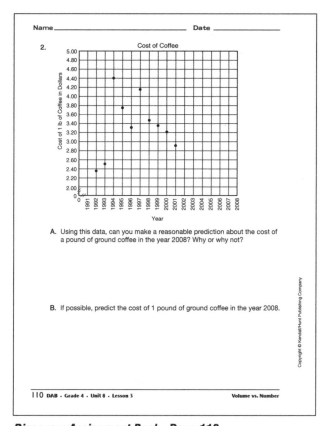

Discovery Assignment Book - Page 110

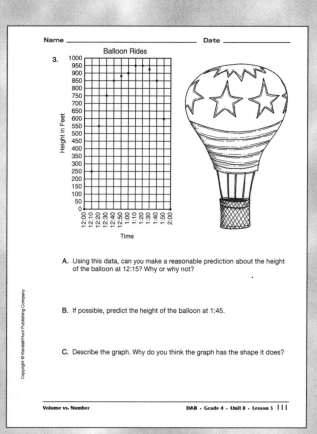

Discovery Assignment Book - Page 111

AT A GLANCE

Math Facts and Daily Practice and Problems

DPP items E–G and I provide practice with math facts. DPP item H is an exercise using perimeter and area. DPP Task J provides practice with estimating volume.

Part 1. Introducing the Lab, Identifying the Variables, and Drawing the Picture

1. Students read the Planning the Experiment section of the *Volume vs. Number* Lab Pages in the *Student Guide*. *Questions 1–4* help students identify the variables in the experiment.
2. Students draw a picture of the experiment that shows the procedure and identifies the variables.

Part 2. Collecting the Data

1. Students fill in the column headings in the *Two-column Data Tables,* choose values for the number of marbles, and write these values in the first column of the tables.
2. Students collect data for two sizes of marbles.

Part 3. Graphing the Data

1. Students plot the data for both sizes of marbles on a single sheet of *Centimeter Graph Paper* in *Questions 5–6.*
2. They draw best-fit lines in *Question 7.*

Part 4. Exploring the Data

1. Students answer *Questions 8–10* in the *Student Guide.* If a group finds that their predicted volume for *Question 10* is not close to their measured volume, they check their data and graph for errors.
2. Students complete *Questions 11–15.* They will need complete experiment setups to check solutions.
3. Review the Student Rubric: *Solving* with students.
4. Students write their solutions to *Question 12.*

Homework

1. Assign the *Predicting Prices* Activity Pages in the *Discovery Assignment Book.*
2. Assign Parts 2 and 3 of the Home Practice.
3. Assign the *Review Problems* Activity Pages in Lesson 4 of the *Student Guide.*

Assessment

1. Use the *Observational Assessment Record* to note students' skills measuring volume by displacement.
2. Use the Assessment section of the *Teacher Implementation Guide* to provide a framework for scoring the *Volume vs. Number* lab.
3. Use *Question 12* to assess students' problem-solving abilities. Score their work using the Solving dimension of the *TIMS Multidimensional Rubric.*
4. Students add their labs to their collection folders.

Notes:

Student Guide

Questions 1–15 (SG pp. 226–229)

1. *N, Number of Marbles and V, Volume

2. **A.** *N, Number of Marbles; The values for the number of marbles are chosen at the beginning of the experiments.

   B. *V, Volume; Students find the volume as a result of the experiments.

   C. N and V

3. *size of marble

4. **A.** *2, 4, and 8 marbles

   B. *These values show doubling patterns.

   C. Answers will vary.

5. *See Figure 8 in Lesson Guide 3 for a sample graph.

6. *0 cc

7. **A.–B.** *See Figure 8 in Lesson Guide 3 for a sample graph.

8. Marbles have a volume as does the water. The marbles displace or push up the water, which causes the water level to rise.

9. Answers will vary. The line for the larger marbles goes uphill faster than the line for the smaller marbles. They both include the point for $N=0$ and $V=0$ and slant uphill.

10. **A.** *Based on the graph in Figure 8 of the Lesson Guide, about 12 cc.

    B. *Answers will vary. Based on the graph in Figure 8, interpolation.

    C.–E. *Answers will vary.

11. **A.** *Based on the graph in Figure 8 of the Lesson Guide, about 28 cc.

    B. *Answers will vary. Based on the graph in Figure 8, extrapolation.

    C.–D. Answers will vary.

12. **A.** *Answers will vary. Using the graph in Figure 8, the volume of 24 marbles is about 44 cc. Since the volume of 12 marbles is 22 cc, the volume of 24 marbles will be about double that.

    B.–C. Answers will vary.

13. *Answers will vary. Based on sample graph, 33 cc. See Figure 8 in Lesson Guide 3.

14. *Answers will vary. See Figure 8 in Lesson Guide 3. The volume of the marbles is $168 - 150 = 18$ cc. Using the sample graph, the number of marbles is 5.

15. Keenya drew line B. Her marbles have less volume than Jacob's marbles.

Discovery Assignment Book

**Home Practice (DAB pp. 93–94)

Part 2. Number Relationships

Questions 1–3

Explanations will vary for Questions 1 and 2.

1. **A.** No. $3 \times 17 = 51$

   B. Yes. Its only factors are 1 and 53.

   C. No. $55 \div 5 = 11$

2. **A.** Yes. 6 divides 96 evenly; $96 \div 6 = 16$; The sum of the digits of 96 $(9 + 6 = 15)$ is a multiple of 3. 96 is also an even number. Since it is divisible by 2 and 3, it is divisible by 6.

   B. No. 6 does not divide 116 evenly; $116 \div 6 = 19.333 \ldots$ See explanation for 2A.

3. Answers will vary. One possible factor tree is shown.

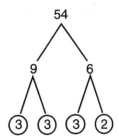

---

*Answers and/or discussion are included in the Lesson Guide.

**Answers for all the Home Practice in the *Discovery Assignment Book* are at the end of the unit.

Part 3. Performing Operations

Questions 1–5

1. **A.** 1228
   B. 6576
   C. 4296
   D. 190
   E. 63,000
   F. 264

2. $262

3. Estimates will vary. $30 \times 70 = 2100$ points

4. Estimates will vary.
   $45,000,000 - 40,000,000 = 5,000,000$ votes

5. 88 days

Predicting Prices (DAB pp. 109–111)

Questions 1–3

1. Note that the point for 1994 is not used in drawing a best-fit line, since something unusual happened to the price in 1994. This kind of point is called an "outlier." Student lines will vary based on how they interpret this point.

   A. Answers will vary. Some students may feel that the points jump around too much to make a good prediction for the cost of lettuce. Others may use a best-fit line to make a prediction.

   B. Between 90¢ and $1.00

   C. Answers will vary. The lettuce crop may have frozen and less lettuce was available. Thus, the cost went up.

2. **A.** No. The price varies too much to make a prediction.

   B. Not possible to make a reasonable prediction. Students may predict the price will be anywhere from $2.50 and $4.50!

3. **A.** Yes; Although the points do not form a line, there is a pattern. The points form a curve. About 450 feet

   B. About 725 feet

   C. Descriptions will vary. The graph has the shape it does because the balloon goes up, then comes down.

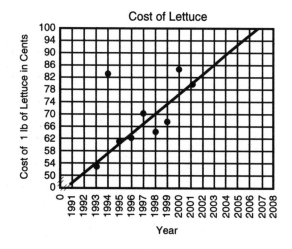

*Answers and/or discussion are included in the Lesson Guide.

**Answers for all the Home Practice in the *Discovery Assignment Book* are at the end of the unit.

58 URG • Grade 4 • Unit 8 • Lesson 3 • Answer Key

LESSON GUIDE Review Problems

 Estimated Class Sessions: 1

This lesson provides practice and review of the skills and concepts that have been studied in Units 1 through 7 of Grade 4. Students have an opportunity to refresh their skills and identify those areas they may need to review prior to taking the *Midyear Test* in Lesson 6.

Key Content

- Reviewing skills and concepts.

OPTIONAL LESSON

There are no Daily Practice and Problems items for this lesson.

Materials List

Print Materials for Students

	Homework
Student Guide	*Review Problems* Pages 230–231

Student Book

Supplies for Each Student

ruler
calculator

Review Problems

You will need a ruler and a calculator to complete the problems.

1. Make a factor tree to find the prime factors for the following numbers.
   A. 28   B. 124   C. 125

2. Solve the following problems in Question 2 without a calculator.

   A.   1267   B.   17,146   C.   3000
      +1499   −   459   ×9

   D.   49   E.   500   F.   70
        ×7   ×8   ×60

3. Write the following numbers using base-ten shorthand.
   A. 467   B. 7615   C. 1042

4. Tell what the circled digit stands for in each of the following problems. The circled digit in the example stands for 30 or 3 tens.

   Example:

   1③2
   +79

   A. 20,004   B.   4236   C.   ①
        ×7   +2④49   1278
       2⑧   +5053
                                       1

5. Find the median for this set of numbers: 12, 15, 17, 13, 9, 25, 12, 17. Then, use a calculator to find the mean.

6. Write each of the following numbers in words.
   A. 1214   B. 77,589   C. 134,121

7. Write the following as numbers.
   A. two thousand twenty-four
   B. forty-four thousand, three hundred sixty-nine
   C. two hundred sixty-five thousand, three hundred twenty-eight

Student Guide - Page 230

---

8. Label the following angles as acute, right, or obtuse.

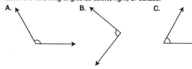

   A.   B.   C.

9. Find the area of the following shape in square inches.

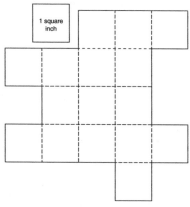

1 square inch

10. Find the perimeter of the shape.

11. Solve the given fact. Then write all the other number sentences in the same fact family.
    A. 28 ÷ 4 =   B. 7 × 7 =

Student Guide - Page 231

Developing the Lesson

This set of problems may be used as class work or assigned as homework. It provides practice and review before students take the *Midyear Test* in Lesson 6. Students can work on these problems independently, so as to approximate the actual test-taking conditions or they can work on them in groups and compare solutions. After the problems are completed, have the students discuss their solutions and solution strategies with the class. Make sure students have ample opportunity to ask for clarification of any problems with which they had difficulty.

Suggestions for Teaching the Lesson

Homework and Practice

These problems may be assigned for homework.

Developing the Activity

Students complete the *Review Problems* in the *Student Guide.* This problem set provides review for the *Midyear Test.*

Homework

The *Review Problems* may be assigned for homework.

Notes:

Student Guide

Questions 1–11 (SG pp. 230–231)

1. **A.–C.** Answers will vary. One possible factor tree is shown for each.

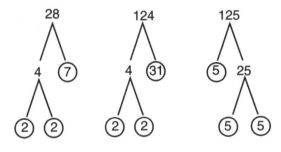

2. **A.** 2766
   B. 16,687
   C. 27,000
   D. 343
   E. 4000
   F. 4200

3. **A.**

   B.

   C.

4. **A.** 8 or 8 ones
   B. 400
   C. 10

5. 14; 15

6. **A.** one thousand two hundred fourteen
   B. seventy-seven thousand, five hundred eighty-nine
   C. one hundred thirty-four thousand, one hundred twenty-one

7. **A.** 2024
   B. 44,369
   C. 265,328

8. **A.** obtuse
   B. right
   C. acute

9. 16 square inches

10. 24 inches

11. **A.** 7; $28 \div 7 = 4$; $4 \times 7 = 28$; $7 \times 4 = 28$
    B. 49; $49 \div 7 = 7$

---

*Answers and/or discussion are included in the Lesson Guide.

**Answers for all the Home Practice in the *Discovery Assignment Book* are at the end of the unit.

Daily Practice and Problems:
Bit for Lesson 5

K. Taking Medicine (URG p. 15)

When Jerome had a sore throat, his doctor
told his parents to give Jerome 1 teaspoon of
medicine three times a day for 10 days. One
teaspoon is about 5 ml (1 ml = 1 cc).

1. About how many cubic centimeters (cc)
    of medicine did he take each day?

2. About how many cubic centimeters (cc)
    did he take in 10 days?

DPP Task is on page 72. Suggestions for using the
DPPs are on page 72.

LESSON GUIDE 5
Hour Walk

Estimated Class Sessions: 1–2

In this assessment activity, students estimate the number of steps they would take
if they walked for one hour. After reading
the problem, they devise, carry out, and
communicate their problem-solving strategies.

Key Content

*   Solving open-response problems.
*   Communicating problem-solving strategies.
*   Collecting and using data to solve problems.
*   Solving problems involving multiplication and
    division.
*   Using the Student Rubrics: *Knowing, Solving,*
    and *Telling* to self-assess problem-solving skills.

Curriculum Sequence

Before This Unit

Problem Solving. Students solved open-response problems using student rubrics as a guide in Units 2, 5, and 7.
If students' solutions to these problems have been included in their portfolios, their work on the problem in this
lesson can be compared to earlier work. Growth in students' abilities to solve problems and communicate solutions can be documented.

After This Unit

Problem Solving. Students will continue to solve open-response problems during the remainder of fourth
grade. See Unit 12 Lesson 8 and Unit 16 Lesson 3 for specific examples.

Materials List

Print Materials for Students

	Math Facts and Daily Practice and Problems	Assessment Activity	Homework	Written Assessment
Student Books — Student Guide		Student Rubrics: *Knowing* Appendix A, *Solving* Appendix B, and *Telling* Appendix C and Inside Back Cover ⊙		
Student Books — Discovery Assignment Book			Home Practice Parts 4 & 5 Pages 95–96	
Teacher Resource — Unit Resource Guide	DPP Items K–L Pages 15–16 ⊙			*Hour Walk* Page 74, 1 per sudent

⊙ available on Teacher Resource CD

All Transparency Masters, Blackline Masters, and Assessment Blackline Masters in the Unit Resource Guide are on the Teacher Resource CD.

Supplies for Each Student Group

classroom clock or stopwatch
calculators

Materials for the Teacher

TIMS Multidimensional Rubric (Teacher Implementation Guide, Assessment section)
Transparencies or posters of *Solving, Telling,* and *Knowing* Student Rubrics (Teacher Implementation Guide, Assessment section), optional

Developing the Activity

To begin the activity, students read and discuss the problem on the *Hour Walk* Assessment Blackline Master. Groups of three or four students work well for this activity since they will need to collect data to solve the problem. However, since this is an assessment activity, groups should formulate and carry out their plans without consulting you, except to ask for clarification of the problem.

Once the groups reach a solution, encourage them to write clear explanations of their problem-solving process. Groups can work together to write an explanation or each student can write his or her own report.

To make your expectations clear, review one or more of the student rubrics and inform students that their work will be scored using those rubrics. As students work, observe those students who need help getting organized or need help devising an efficient strategy. For example, you may need to encourage a group to walk for a short period of time and use the data to estimate an answer, rather than actually walking for an hour. If you need to intervene, keep notes and adjust student scores accordingly.

When students have completed writing their explanations, give them an opportunity to revise their work based on your comments. For example, students may need to be reminded to include units or report their data in an organized fashion. Or, you may need to advise them to explain their method more clearly. Your observations can be used as you score students' work.

A discussion of exemplary student work may help students understand the writing process better. You can make transparencies of student work from previous classes or from the Lesson Guide that clearly communicates efficient problem-solving strategies. Then, ask students to critique the work using the student rubrics as guides.

Students should add this assessment to their collection folders and compare their work on *Hour Walk* to efforts on similar tasks such as *A Letter to Myrna* from Unit 2, *Professor Peabody Invents a Ball* from Unit 5, or *The Broken Calculator* from Unit 7.

Content Note

This task was originally listed as a possible test item in a National Council of Teachers of Mathematics publication in 1941. The author, William Brownell, wrote a chapter for the sixteenth annual yearbook entitled, "The Evaluation of Learning in Arithmetic." In the chapter he presents many ideas on evaluation of student performance in arithmetic that are also advocated in current literature on mathematics education.

Journal Prompt

Explain how your group worked on the problem together. What did each member of the group do to help?

The following discussion provides four examples of student work with scores for each dimension of the multidimensional rubric. To assist you in scoring your students' work, questions specific to this task are listed here:

Solving

- Are the strategies complete and efficient? For example, do they include gathering data on the number of steps taken in a short period of time?

- Did students organize their data?

- Did students use previously encountered mathematics and scientific processes such as averaging data from multiple trials and controlling variables that should be held fixed?

- Did they stick with the problem until they had collected enough data and arrived at a solution?

- Did they look back at the problem to check for the reasonableness of their results, looking to see if their data is accurate and that the results of their calculations are reasonable? Do they solve the problem in more than one way?

Knowing

- Did students choose appropriate operations and procedures?

- Did students compute accurately, use the calculator effectively, or use efficient estimation strategies?

- Did they time their steps accurately, using the clock or stopwatch correctly?

- Did students apply mathematical knowledge such as the number of minutes in an hour or the procedure for finding a mean or median?

Telling

- Did students clearly describe all of their strategies? Did they explain or draw a picture of their procedures?

- Did they explain why they chose an operation or a value? For example, if they multiplied the number of steps by 12, did they explain that they walked for 5 minutes and 5 minutes is one-twelfth of an hour?

- Did they use appropriate number sentences or other symbolic representations?

- Did they use a data table to organize and display their data?

- Did they use units such as minutes and hours?

The following samples of student work have been scored using these criteria.

Scoring Keenya's work

5,000 is closest to our answer

1,059 steps 105 steps
10:00 min. 1:00 min.

My partner and I walked for 10 min. We both got exactly 1,059 steps since we both have the same answer we don't have to averge out our work 10 x 6 is 60 and thiesa re 60 min. in an hour we multiply 10,59 x 6 = 6,354 step thats one of our answer

if we walked 1 hour

We also walked for 1 min. Again we got the same answer. It was 105 steps. 1x60 = 60, 6 min is a hour so we multiplyed 105 x 60. We got 6,350 steps that's our other answer for how many steps it would take for 1 hour. We know we our close because the our answers are only 4 steps away We can find a better answer if we average out our 2 answers First we added

Time	How many steps	answer
10 min	1,059	6,354
1 min.	105	6,350

$$\begin{array}{r} 6354 \\ +6350 \\ \hline 12,704 \end{array}$$

than we divided

$$\begin{array}{r} 12,704 \\ \div\ 2 \\ \hline 6,352 \end{array}$$

This is the best answer we can come up with.

Figure 9: *Keenya's work*

The notations used to score Keenya's work on the three dimensions of the rubric are shown in Figure 10.

Solving	Level 4	Level 3	Level 2	Level 1
Identifies the elements of the problem and their relationships to one another	All major elements identified	Most elements identified	Some, but shows little understanding of relationships	Few or none
Uses problem-solving strategies which are…	Systematic, complete, efficient, and possibly elegant	Systematic and nearly complete, but not efficient	Incomplete or unsystematic	Not evident or inappropriate
Organizes relevant information…	Systematically and efficiently	Systematically, with minor errors	Unsystematically	Not at all
Relates the problem and solution to previously encountered mathematics and makes connections that are…	At length, elegant, and meaningful	Evident	Brief or logically unsound	Not evident
Persists in the problem-solving process…	At length	Until a solution is reached	Briefly	Not at all
Looks back to examine the reasonableness of the solution and draws conclusions that are…	Insightful and comprehensive	Correct	Incorrect or logically unsound	Not present

Knowing	Level 4	Level 3	Level 2	Level 1
Understands the task's mathematical concepts, their properties and applications…	Completely	Nearly completely	Partially	Not at all
Translates between words, pictures, symbols, tables, graphs, and real situations…	Readily and without errors	With minor errors	With major errors	Not at all
Uses tools (measuring devices, graphs, tables, calculators, etc.) and procedures…	Correctly and efficiently	Correctly or with minor errors	Incorrectly	Not at all
Uses knowledge of the facts of mathematics (geometry definitions, math facts, etc.)…	Correctly	With minor errors	With major errors	Not at all

Telling	Level 4	Level 3	Level 2	Level 1
Includes response with an explanation and/or description which is…	Complete and clear	Fairly complete and clear	Perhaps ambiguous or unclear	Totally unclear or irrelevant
Presents supporting arguments which are…	Strong and sound	Logically sound, but may contain minor gaps	Incomplete or logically unsound	Not present
Uses pictures, symbols, tables, and graphs which are…	Correct and clearly relevant	Present with minor errors or somewhat irrelevant	Present with errors and/or irrelevant	Not present or completely inappropriate
Uses terminology…	Clearly and precisely	With minor errors	With major errors	Not at all

Figure 10: *Using the* TIMS Multidimensional Rubric *to score Keenya's work on all three dimensions*

Solving: 3

Keenya and her partner identified most of the elements of the problem. They collected data, averaged the results, and used their data to make a prediction. However, they did not recognize that it was not necessary to find an exact answer and therefore their strategies were not completely efficient. It would have been more efficient to round the number of steps. Their procedures for collecting the data are suspect since each partner counted exactly the same number of steps. They did organize their data in a table, although without headings, the first table is not completely clear. The strength of their problem-solving strategies lies in the extent to which the girls persisted in the process. They first solved the problem using two different methods, then compared the two to check the reasonableness of their results. They then averaged the two solutions to find "a better answer."

Knowing: 3

Keenya and her partner nearly understood the task. However, as mentioned above, they did not see that the problem could be solved more efficiently by using round numbers to make their estimates. They used symbols relatively well in the description of their calculations. However, they did not correctly write their division sentence and they made minor errors such as writing "6 min is a hour" once and multiplying incorrectly ($105 \times 60 = 6300$, not 6350).

Telling: 4

Keenya's description of her group's problem-solving process is complete and clear. She justified their choice of operations and use of averages. We know that she and her partner chose to solve the problem in two ways to check their results. She displayed the data in a table, used terminology (average, multiplied, etc.) clearly, and used correct units appropriately.

Scoring Grace's work

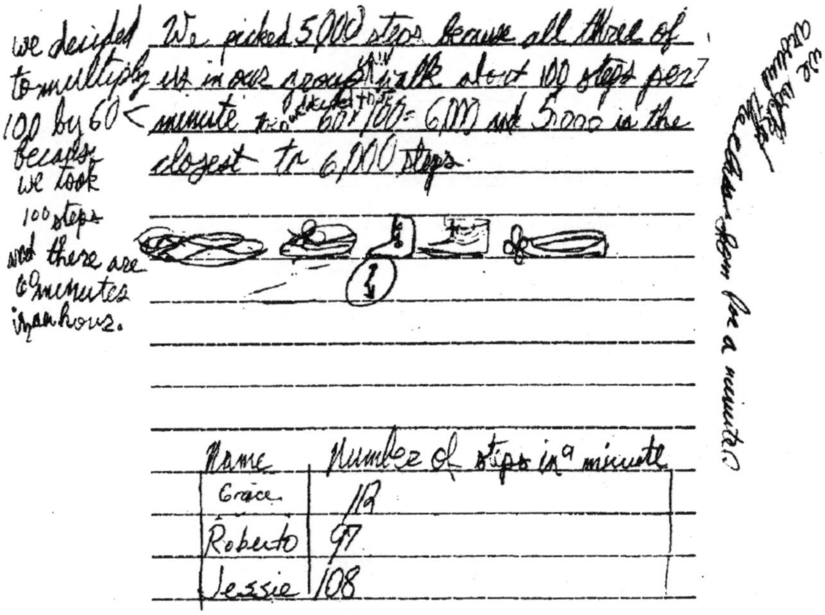

Figure 11: *Grace's work*

Solving: 3

Grace's group found the number of steps each member of the group walked in one minute and organized their work in a data table. The solution includes the use of multiple trials, estimation, and multiplication. Instead of calculating an average of the three trials, she looked at the data and estimated that they each walked "about 100 steps." Since the problem only asks for an estimate, this choice of a convenient number for an estimate is appropriate. There is no evidence that she looked back at her work to check the reasonableness of the results.

Knowing: 4

As stated above, Grace used data from three trials to estimate that her group could walk 100 steps in one minute. Then, she correctly multiplied 60 times 100, telling us that there are 60 minutes in one hour.

Telling: 3

Grace used a picture, data table, and number sentence as part of her written explanation of her group's solution. The data table is clearly labeled, and the picture identifies the important variables of the problem as time and steps. She explained that they walked around the room for a minute and, with a prompt from the teacher, told us that they multiplied the number of steps by 60 because there are 60 minutes in one hour.

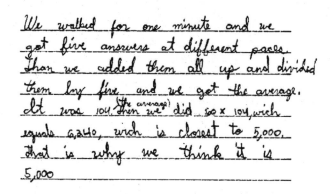

We walked for one minute and we got five answers at different paces. Than we added them all up and divided them by five and we got the average. It was 104. Then we (the average) did 60 × 104, wich equals 6,240, wich is closest to 5,000. That is why we think it is 5,000

Figure 12: *Michael's work*

Solving: 3

Michael's group devised a plan and carried it out until a solution was reached. He used previously encountered mathematics when he took five trials and found the average of the results, although he did not present his data in an organized fashion. There is no evidence that he looked back at his calculations to check his answer.

Knowing: 3

Michael chose appropriate operations and procedures: taking five trials, averaging, reading a clock, multiplying, and estimating. However, we don't know if his calculations are correct since he didn't report the results of the five trials.

Telling: 2

Michael's sentences are very clear, using math terms such as "average" correctly, so that we can understand the group's procedure. However, he did not display his data in any way, use units, or tell us why he chose to multiply by 60.

Scoring Roberto's work

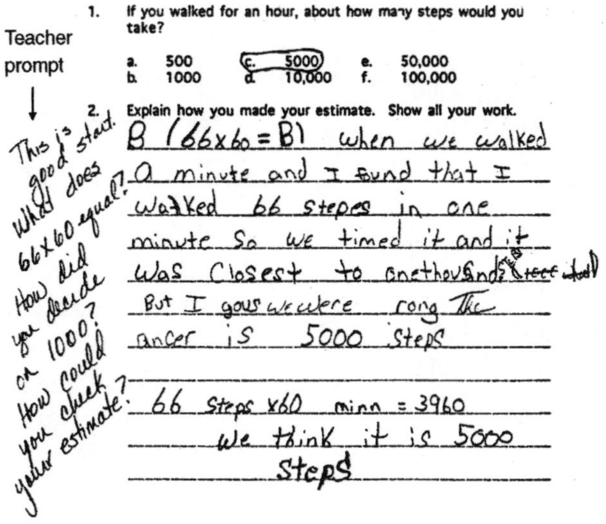
Teacher prompt

1. If you walked for an hour, about how many steps would you take?

a. 500 b. 1000 c. 5000 d. 10,000 e. 50,000 f. 100,000

2. Explain how you made your estimate. Show all your work.

B (66x60 = B) when we walked a minute and I found that I walked 66 steps in one minute So we timed it and it was Closest to onethousands But I gous we were rong The ancer is 5000 steps

66 steps x60 minn = 3960 we think it is 5000 steps

This is good start. What does 66x60 equal? How did you decide on 1000? How could you check your estimate?

Figure 13: *Roberto's work*

Solving: 2

The process Roberto used is not as sophisticated as the first three students' strategies. His group did not take more than one trial or average any data.

Knowing: 2

Roberto correctly chose to multiply the number of steps by 60, but until prompted by the teacher to revise his work, he either multiplied 66 × 60 incorrectly or did not realize that 3960 is closer to 5000 than 1000.

Telling: 2

We understand from Roberto's revised explanation that his group first made one estimate, then decided that they made a mistake. They showed their new calculations using a number sentence with all the numbers labeled correctly. However, at least one sentence ("So we timed it and it was closest to one thousand.") is unclear. What did they time that was close to one thousand? Also, he did not explain why they "think it is 5000 steps."

Daily Practice and Problems: Task for Lesson 5

L. Task: Estimating Volume Again (URG p. 16)

1. Estimate the volume of the jar your teacher shows you. Write down your estimate and be ready to share your estimation strategy with the class.

2. After everyone has made his or her estimate, a student from the class will find the volume of the jar using a graduated cylinder.

3. Find 10% of the measured volume of the jar. Is your estimated volume within 10% of the measured volume? Show how you know.

Suggestions for Teaching the Lesson

Math Facts

Encourage students to study for the *Multiplication Facts Inventory Test* for homework (see Lesson 8). Remind them to use their flash cards and study 8–10 facts at a time.

Homework and Practice

- Students can revise their explanations for homework.
- DPP items K and L provide practice with estimation and measurement.
- Parts 4 and 5 of the Home Practice may be assigned for homework. Part 4 is an arithmetic review. Part 5 provides practice with large numbers.

Answers for Parts 4 and 5 of the Home Practice can be found in the Answer Key at the end of this lesson and at the end of this unit.

Assessment

Use the *TIMS Multidimensional Rubric* and the Student Rubrics: *Solving, Telling,* and *Knowing* to assess students' abilities to solve open-response problems and communicate their solution strategies.

Name _____ Date _____

Part 4 Arithmetic Review

1. Use paper and pencil or mental math to solve the following problems. Estimate to make sure your answers make sense.

   A. $6035 - 854 =$ B. $64 \times 8 =$ C. $47 \times 8 =$

   D. $437 + 579 + 902 =$ E. $3649 - 2089 =$ F. $82 \times 5 =$

2. Explain your estimation strategy for Question 1C.

3. Use estimation to answer Questions 3A and 3B. Record number sentences to show what convenient numbers you chose. Then, solve the problem in Question 3C.

   A. Maya has $10.00 to buy the following items: cereal for $3.28, milk for $2.89, and bread for $1.56. Estimate to see if she has enough money. If there is no sales tax, about how much change will Maya receive from her $10 bill or about how much more money will she need?

   B. Shannon has been given $15.00 to buy school supplies. She wants to buy 5 notebooks that cost $1.25 each, 10 pencils that cost 19 cents each, and 4 folders that cost 28 cents each. Estimate to see if she has enough money. About how much money will she have left? Or, how much extra will she need based on your estimation?

   C. Jerome's aunt gave him $20.00 for his birthday present. He purchased a shirt for $7.99, a cap for $2.60, and socks. After shopping, he had $5.67 left over. If no tax was paid, what was the exact cost of the socks? Look back at your answer. Is it reasonable?

Discovery Assignment Book - Page 95

Name _____ Date _____

Part 5 Base-Ten Shorthand

1. The bit is one whole. Label each of the following with its correct number. Then, put the numbers in order from least to greatest.

   A.
   B.
   C.
   D.

2. The following information, taken from the *1996 World Almanac*, shows the number of people employed in various occupations in the United States.

Crafts people and those who repair things:	10,435,000 people
Farming, forestry, and fishing:	1,430,000 people
Machine operators and truck drivers:	14,001,000 people
Professionals (accountants, doctors, lawyers, teachers, nurses):	23,247,000 people
Sales people, technicians, administrative workers:	25,928,000 people
Service jobs such as waiters, guards, and janitors:	9,104,000 people

   A. List the number of people employed in the different kinds of jobs in order from least to greatest.

   B. About 3,383,000 of the machine operators and truck drivers are women. About how many are men?

   C. About 12,082,000 of the professionals are men. About how many are women?

Discovery Assignment Book - Page 96

AT A GLANCE

Math Facts and Daily Practice and Problems

DPP items K and L provide practice with estimation and measurement.

Developing the Activity

1. Students read the problem on the *Hour Walk* Assessment Blackline Master.
2. Advise students that their work will be scored using one or more of the rubrics. Review these student rubrics.
3. Students work on the problem in groups of three or four and write their explanations.
4. Students revise their work based on your comments.
5. Score students' work using one or more of the dimensions of the *TIMS Multidimensional Rubric.*
6. Students add their papers to their collection folders.

Homework

1. Students can complete their explanations for homework.
2. Students study for the *Multiplication Facts Inventory Test* in Lesson 8.
3. Parts 4 and 5 of the Home Practice may be assigned for homework.

Notes:

Hour Walk

If you walked steadily for an hour, about how many steps would you take?

A. 500   **B.** 1000   **C.** 5000   **D.** 10,000   **E.** 50,000   **F.** 100,000

Make an estimate without walking for one hour. Explain how you made your estimate. Show all your work.

Discovery Assignment Book

**Home Practice (DAB pp. 95–96)

Part 4. Arithmetic Review

Questions 1–3

1. **A.** 5181
   B. 512
   C. 376
   D. 1918
   E. 1560
   F. 410

2. Possible strategy: $50 \times 8 = 400$

3. **A.** Answers will vary. She has enough money: $3.25 + $3.00 + $1.50 = $7.75. She will receive about $2.25 in change.

   B. Answers will vary. She has enough money. She will receive between $5.00 and $7.00 in change.

   C. $3.74

Part 5. Base-Ten Shorthand

Questions 1–2

1. **A.** 2045
   B. 254
   C. 1158
   D. 2100; Numbers in order: 254, 1158, 2045, 2100

2. **A.** 1,430,000; 9,104,000; 10,435,000; 14,001,000; 23,247,000; 25,928,000

   B. Estimates will vary.
   14,000,000 – 3,000,000 = 11,000,000 men

   C. Estimates will vary.
   23,000,000 – 12,000,000 = 11,000,000 women

Unit Resource Guide

Hour Walk (URG p. 74)

See the Lesson Guide for sample student work and scoring on the rubric.

*Answers and/or discussion are included in the Lesson Guide.

**Answers for all the Home Practice in the *Discovery Assignment Book* are at the end of the unit.

M. Facts Practice (URG p. 16)

Solve the given fact. Then, name the other related fact or facts in the same fact family.

A. $2 \times 8 =$ _____   B. $64 \div 8 =$ _____

C. $24 \div 6 =$ _____   D. $5 \times 9 =$ _____

E. $4 \times 4 =$ _____   F. $63 \div 9 =$ _____

G. $7 \times 3 =$ _____   H. $27 \div 3 =$ _____

O. Languages Spoken at Home (URG p. 18)

In 2000, about 28,101,052 people over the age of 5 spoke Spanish at home in the United States.

2,022,143 people spoke Chinese.

1,643,838 spoke French.

1,383,442 spoke German.

667,414 spoke Polish.

706,242 spoke Russian.

1,224,241 spoke Tagalog.

1. Write the seven numbers in order from largest to smallest.

2. About how many more people spoke Spanish than French?

3. About how many more people spoke Russian than Polish?

4. About how many more people spoke German than Tagalog?

DPP Task and Challenge are on page 79. Suggestions for using the DPPs are on page 79.

LESSON GUIDE 6
Midyear Test

Estimated Class Sessions: 2

Students take a paper-and-pencil test. These items test skills and concepts studied in Units 1–8.

Key Content

- Assessing concepts and skills developed in Units 1–8.

Materials List

Print Materials for Students

		Math Facts and Daily Practice and Problems	Written Assessment
Teacher Resources	**Facts Resource Guide**	DPP Item 8M	
	Unit Resource Guide	DPP Items M–P Pages 16–19	*Midyear Test* Pages 81–86, 1 per student

⊙ *available on Teacher Resource CD*

All Transparency Masters, Blackline Masters, and Assessment Blackline Masters in the Unit Resource Guide are on the Teacher Resource CD.

Supplies for Each Student

ruler
calculator
square-inch tiles

Before the Activity

Look over the problems on the test before administering it. If you chose not to complete some of the activities in Units 1–8, omit test items that use content from the skipped activities.

Developing the Activity

Students take the test individually. The test is divided into two parts. Each part will take one class session. The problems in Part 1 assess students' knowledge of the order of operations, their fluency with multidigit addition and subtraction, their abilities to solve multiplication problems, and their estimation skills. Students should complete these items without a calculator.

Students will need a ruler and a calculator to complete Part 2 of the test. They will use rulers to draw best-fit lines and they will use calculators for finding averages and making other calculations. Square-inch tiles should be available for students to use, since a few of the items ask questions involving the tiles. Remind students that using tools and manipulatives is a good problem-solving technique.

Students should follow directions given for each question. Remind students to give full explanations of their problem-solving strategies.

Suggestions for Teaching the Lesson

Math Facts

DPP Bit M provides practice for the multiplication and division facts through the use of fact families.

Homework and Practice

- DPP Task N provides practice with addition and subtraction using either mental math or paper and pencil. Bit O provides practice with large numbers. Challenge P requires students to read a scenario involving time and organize the information.

- For homework, students use their *Triangle Flash Cards* to study for the *Multiplication Facts Inventory Test* in Lesson 8.

Assessment

Place students' tests in their collection folders.

Daily Practice and Problems:
Task & Challenge for Lesson 6

N. Task: Arithmetic Review
  (URG p. 17)

Solve the following problems using paper and pencil or mental math. Estimate to make sure your answers make sense.

1. A. 3048   B.   6007   C.   9015
      + 253   − 824   +6386

   D. 3005 + 61 + 458 =

   E. 17 + 608 + 3 + 1060 =

   F. 917 − 145 =

2. Explain how you solved Question 1B.

P. Challenge: Never too Late!
  (URG p. 19)

The school bell rang at 8:25 A.M. Maya arrived 10 minutes early and played with Irma. Irma had already been playing for 20 minutes. When Luis arrived, he joined Irma, but he had to wait about 4 minutes until Maya arrived. Linda arrived 6 minutes before the bell.

1. Tell the order and the time each child arrived at school.

2. How many minutes had gone by from the time the first student arrived until the last student arrived?

AT A GLANCE

Math Facts and Daily Practice and Problems

DPP Bit M provides practice with the multiplication and division facts. Task N provides practice with addition and subtraction. Bit O involves working with large numbers. Challenge P involves organizing a series of time statements.

Developing the Activity

1. Students take Part 1 of the test without using calculators.
2. Students take Part 2 of the test. Students may use calculators, a ruler, square-inch tiles, base-ten pieces, or any other tools.

Homework

For homework, students study for the *Multiplication Facts Inventory Test.*

Assessment

Place students' tests in their collection folders.

Notes:

Midyear Test

Part 1

You may not use your calculator on Part 1. You may use your calculator on Part 2.

1. The sixth-graders at Coleman School want to save soup can labels to buy kickballs. They need 4500 labels. So far, they have collected 2340 labels. How many more labels do they need?

2. The fourth-graders have collected 3476 soup can labels to be used to buy playground equipment. The third-graders have collected 1789 labels.

   A. How many labels do the third- and fourth-graders have altogether?

   B. Which grade collected more labels? How many more labels did they collect?

3. Each school bus has seats for 36 students. There are 290 students going on a field trip. Will 8 buses be enough to take all 290 students on the trip? Why or why not?

4. $6 \times 4 - 15 \div 3 = ?$

5. Complete the following problems. Estimate to be sure your answers are reasonable.

   A. 8156
       + 7997

   B. 6047
       + 554

   C. 27,854
       − 2356

   D. Explain your estimation strategy for Question 5B.

E. $80 \times 400 =$

F. $4000 \times 5 =$

G. $\begin{array}{r} 69 \\ \times\ 4 \\ \hline \end{array}$

H. $\begin{array}{r} 76 \\ \times\ 5 \\ \hline \end{array}$

6. The table below lists the area of each of the National Parks in the state of Utah. Use the information in the table to answer the following questions.

National Park	Area
Arches	76,518 acres
Bryce Canyon	35,835 acres
Canyon Lands	337,598 acres
Capitol Reef	241,904 acres
Zion	146,592 acres

A. Estimate the total amount of land set aside in Utah as National Park land. Write a number sentence to show your thinking.

B. Which National Park covers about 150,000 square acres?

C. Estimate the difference in size between Capitol Reef National Park and Zion National Park. Write a number sentence to show your thinking.

D. Write the numbers of acres in order from smallest to largest.

7. **A.** Irma solved the addition problem at the right. Why did she write a small 1 above the 6?

$\begin{array}{r} 1 \\ 69 \\ +\ 85 \\ \hline 154 \end{array}$

B. Write the answer to Irma's problem using base-ten shorthand.

Part 2

As you answer questions on the second part of the test, you may use any of the tools you have used in class. For example, you may wish to use a ruler, a calculator, square-inch tiles, or base-ten pieces.

8. This is one square inch.

   A. What is the area of the figure below?

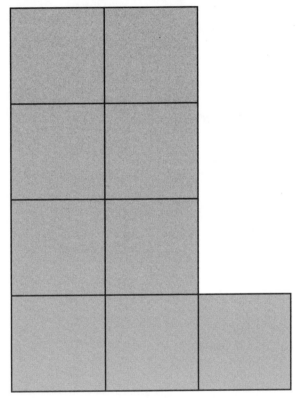

   B. What is the perimeter?

9. Frank is making rectangles with square-inch tiles.

   A. Can he make a rectangle with 4 rows using exactly 21 tiles? Why or why not?

   B. Can he make a rectangle with 3 rows using exactly 21 tiles? Why or why not?

10. **A.** Is 6 a factor of 30? Why or why not?

    B. Is 6 a factor of 32? Why or why not?

11. Make a factor tree to find the prime factors of 60.

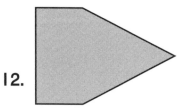

12.

   A. How many right angles does this shape have?
   B. How many acute angles does this shape have?
   C. How many obtuse angles does this shape have?

13. Grace completed the data table at the right. She collected the data from her family.

   A. Find the median hand length.
   B. Use your calculator to find the mean. Give your answer to the nearest cm.

Name	Hand Length in cm
Grace	14 cm
Ben	10 cm
Faith	14 cm
Mom	15 cm

14. Lee Yah found the volume of 1, 2, and 4 large marbles using a graduated cylinder. Then, she graphed her data. Use Lee Yah's graph to answer the questions.

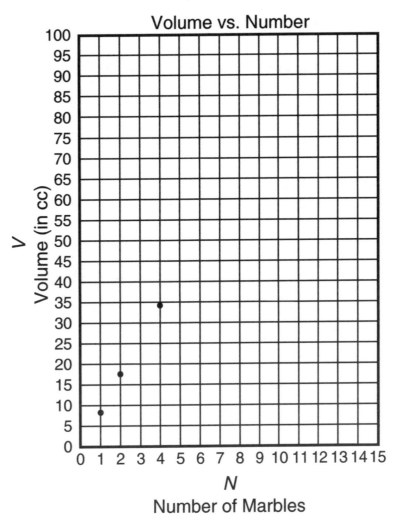

A. Draw a best-fit line.

B. Estimate the volume of three marbles. Show how you made your prediction.

C. Did you use interpolation or extrapolation to answer Question 14B?

D. Predict the volume of six marbles. Show how you made your prediction.

E. Did you use interpolation or extrapolation?

Unit Resource Guide

Midyear Test (URG pp. 81–86)

Questions 1–14

1. 2160 labels

2. **A.** 5265 labels

   B. fourth graders, 1687 labels

3. No. $8 \times 36 = 288$; 8 buses will accommodate all but 2 children.

4. 19

5. **A.** 16,153

   B. 6601

   C. 25,498

   D. Strategies will vary. Possible strategy:
   $6050 + 550 = 6000 + 500 + 100 = 6600$.

   E. 32,000

   F. 20,000

   G. 276

   H. 380

6. **A.** Estimates will vary.
   $80,000 + 40,000 + 300,000 + 250,000 + 150,000 = 820,000$ acres

   B. Zion National Park

   C. Estimates will vary.
   $250,000 - 150,000 = 100,000$ acres

   D. 35,835; 76,518; 146,592; 241,904; 337,598

7. **A.** $9 + 5 = 14$ or 1 ten and 4 ones; She recorded the 1 in the tens' place to remind her to add on one more ten after she adds 6 tens and 8 tens.

   B.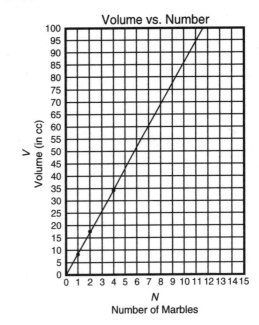

8. **A.** 9 square inches

   B. 14 inches

Explanations will vary for Questions 9 and 10.

9. **A.** No. 4 is not a factor of 21; $21 \div 4 = 5.25$

   B. Yes. 3 is a factor of 21; $21 \div 3 = 7$

10. **A.** Yes. 6 divides 30 evenly; $30 \div 6 = 5$

    B. No. 6 does not divide 32 evenly;
    $32 \div 6 = 5.333$.

11. Answers will vary. One possible factor tree is shown.

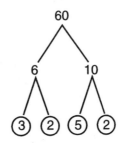

12. **A.** 2

    B. 1

    C. 2

13. **A.** 14 cm

    B. 13 cm

14. **A.**

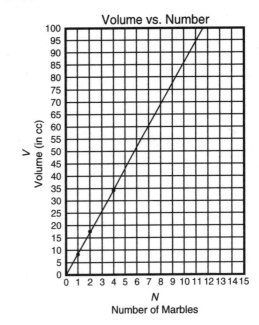

    B. About 25 cc

    C. interpolation

    D. About 51 cc

    E. extrapolation

---

*Answers and/or discussion are included in the Lesson Guide.

**Answers for all the Home Practice in the *Discovery Assignment Book* are at the end of the unit.

LESSON GUIDE

Midyear Experiment and Portfolio Review

Estimated Class Sessions: 2

In Part 1 of this lesson, students review the labs they worked on during the first part of the school year by recording the elements of each lab: variables, number of trials, type of graph, and problems solved. In Part 2, students add assessment tasks from this unit to their portfolios and update the table of contents. They review the contents of their portfolios, comparing old work to new.

Key Content

- Comparing and contrasting the following elements of different labs:
    variables
    measurement procedures
    number of trials
    types of graphs
    problems solved
- Reviewing portfolios.

Curriculum Sequence

Before This Unit

Experiment Review. In Grade 3 Unit 20, students used a similar format to review the labs completed during the school year.

Portfolios. In Unit 2 Lesson 5, students were encouraged to begin collection folders for their portfolios. This lesson also included a procedure for periodically choosing items from the collection folder to add to their portfolios.

After This Unit

Experiment Review. Students will complete an experiment review in Unit 16 reviewing the labs completed in Units 9–16.

Portfolios. Students will continue to save work in their collection folders as the year progresses. They will review this work periodically and choose pieces for inclusion in student portfolios. Work in the portfolios is used to show growth over time.

Materials List

Print Materials for Students

	Math Facts and Daily Practice and Problems	Assessment Activity
Student Books — Student Guide		*Midyear Experiment and Portfolio Review* Pages 232–233
Student Books — Discovery Assignment Book		*Experiment Review Chart* Pages 113–114
Teacher Resources — Facts Resource Guide	DPP Item 8S	
Teacher Resources — Unit Resource Guide	DPP Items Q–T Pages 19–21	

available on Teacher Resource CD

All Transparency Masters, Blackline Masters, and Assessment Blackline Masters in the Unit Resource Guide are on the Teacher Resource CD.

Supplies for Each Student

portfolio
collection folder

Materials for the Teacher

Transparency of *Experiment Review Chart* Activity Pages (Discovery Assignment Book) Pages 113–114

Midyear Experiment and Portfolio Review

This is a good time to review your portfolio. Reviewing the work in your portfolio can help you see how much you have improved in math since the beginning of the year.

Experiment Review

The students in Mrs. Dewey's room were looking back through the labs in their collection folders. Ming found the survey he completed in the beginning of the school year that studied the main interests of his classmates. He decided to compare this work with other labs he had completed during the first half of the year. He organized his work on an *Experiment Review Chart* in the *Discovery Assignment Book*.

Reviewing the labs that you did this year is a good way to help you choose work for your portfolio.

1. Look through your *Student Guide* and your collection folder to help your class make a list of the labs you have completed so far this year.

2. Use the following questions as you review a lab. Record your work on the *Experiment Review Chart*.
   A. What variables did you study in this lab?
   B. Did you have to keep any variables fixed, so that the experiment would be fair? If so, which ones?
   C. Did you measure anything? If so, what did you measure? What units did you use?

Student Guide - Page 232

Developing the Activity

Part 1. Experiment Review

Begin this lesson by reading the introduction on the *Midyear Experiment and Portfolio Review* Activity Pages in the *Student Guide.* Students think about the labs they have completed so far this year and make a class list of these labs. Direct students to look back at work they have saved in their collection folders and at the table of contents at the front of the *Student Guide* to help them generate this list.

> **TIMS Tip**
>
> Remember to include the surveys that students completed in Unit 1 Lessons 1 and 2 in your list. These two activities, while not listed as labs, ask students to collect, organize, graph, and analyze data as they compare two variables.

Choose one lab from the list and review it as a class by answering each part of **Question 2.** You may want to choose one of the survey activities from Unit 1 or *Perimeter vs. Length* from Unit 2. An *Experiment Review Chart* has been included in the *Discovery Assignment Book* to help students organize their information. Have students fill in the title of the lab you will review together at the top of the first column (see Figure 14). They then fill in

---

Name _____ Date _____

Experiment Review Chart

Directions:
- Write the names of the experiments completed this year in the first row of the table.
- Complete each column with information for each lab.

Name of Experiment → / Experiment Elements ↓			
Main Variables			
Fixed Variables			
Anything Measured (units)			
Number of Trials			
Type of Graph			
Important Questions (Answers may vary.)			

Discovery Assignment Book - Page 113

Name _____ Date _____

Directions:
- Write the names of the experiments completed this year in the first row of the table.
- Complete each column with information for each lab.

Name of Experiment → / Experiment Elements ↓			
Main Variables			
Fixed Variables			
Anything Measured (units)			
Number of Trials			
Type of Graph			
Important Questions (Answers may vary.)			

Discovery Assignment Book - Page 114

Name of Experiment → / Experiment Elements ↓	Getting to Know Your Room	Getting to Know Your Room a Little Better	Arm Span vs. Height	Perimeter vs. Length	Bouncing Ball	Volume vs. Number
Main Variables	Answers will vary.	Answers will vary.	A person's arm span, a person's height	Length of runway, perimeter of runway	Drop height of ball, bounce height of ball	Number of marbles, volume of marbles
Fixed Variables	Answers will vary.	Answers will vary.	Procedure used to measure, each person takes off his or her shoes, age of students	Width of runway, type of plane	Type of ball, surface of floor, use the same ball, drop procedure	Type of marble
Anything Measured (units)	No	No	Length of arm span, height, cm or inches	Length of runway, perimeter of runway in cm	Drop height, bounce height, cm	Volume, cubic centimeters
Number of Trials	Not applicable	Not applicable	1	1	3	1
Type of Graph	📊	📊	(scatter plot)	(line graph)	(line graph)	(line graph)
Important Questions (Answers may vary.)	Answers will vary.	Answers will vary.	Is the length of a person's arm span related to his or her height?	How to find the perimeter of a rectangle no matter what the length.	Predict the bounce height given the drop height.	How can you predict the volume of a given number of marbles?

Figure 14: *Sample* Experiment Review Chart

that column with information about the lab. Model this by filling in the appropriate information on a transparency of the *Experiment Review Chart,* as students fill in their charts at their seats.

After this introductory discussion, students complete the review of the remaining labs in groups of two to four students. Assign each group one or two labs on the list and ask them to review the labs using **Question 2** as a guide. Each student should record the information about the lab his or her group is reviewing on the *Experiment Review Chart.*

Once all of the groups have completed their reviews, each group can share their information with the class. Record each group's information on the transparency of the *Experiment Review Chart,* as shown in Figure 14. Your class responses may vary from the responses shown here. Students should also record the information on their own individual charts.

After all of the lab information has been compiled, continue the class discussion by comparing and contrasting various labs. Some possible discussion prompts:

- *When doing an experiment, why do you need to keep some variables fixed?* To be able to look for patterns and make predictions about the main variables in an experiment, other variables must be held fixed. This is often thought of as "keeping the experiment fair." For example, in the experiment *Perimeter vs. Length,* to be able to make predictions about the perimeter of a runway when the length is changed, you must keep the width the same for each runway.

- *Why do we often have to do more than one trial when doing an experiment?* One reason scientists use multiple trials is to check on errors in measurement. Error is often inevitable, so scientists do multiple trials so they can average out the error. For example, in the lab *Bouncing Ball,* students took more than one trial and then used the mean or the median to find a representative value for each trial.

- *How are point graphs used to make estimates and predictions?* If the points suggest a straight line, a line can be drawn that fits the points. This line is called the best-fit line. You can use this line to interpolate and extrapolate information. Students may compare the different point graphs they have done so far. Students may point out that the best-fit line in *Bouncing Ball* and *Number vs. Volume* includes (0,0) as a data point, while the best-fit line in *Perimeter vs. Length* does not include (0,0) as a data point.

- *When is a bar graph appropriate and when is a point graph appropriate?* A bar graph is usually used when one of the variables we are using is categorical or when there are discrete values for our data. For example, it does not make sense to talk about values in between data points for color of hair or number of pets. A point graph is usually used when there are continuous values for the data. For example, it does makes sense to consider values in between data points for the drop height of a bouncing ball, so we plot points and draw a line between the points. The best-fit line is drawn to show where all of the points might be expected to fall.

Students can include the completed *Experiment Review Chart* in their portfolios. It can be used as a reference as they compare labs completed in the second half of the year with those done in the first part of the year.

Part 2. Portfolio Review

This is a good time for students again to review, organize, and add to their portfolios. There are many ways to accomplish this. Specific suggestions for students are given in the *Portfolio Review* section in the *Student Guide.* You may follow these suggestions, or you may choose other activities for your students. See the TIMS Tutor: *Portfolios* in the *Teacher Implementation Guide* for more ideas.

The assessment tasks from previous units and the tasks in this unit make good entries in portfolios. Including these tasks in the students' portfolios will allow you, your students, and their parents to assess growth in mathematics learning over time. For example, student

---

D. How many trials did you do?
E. Describe the shape of your graph.
F. What were the most important problems you solved using your data and your graph?

Portfolio Review

3. If you have not done so recently, choose items from your collection folder to add to your portfolio.

4. Your *Experiment Review Chart* is a good choice for your portfolio.

5. Choose one or two pieces of work from this unit to include in your portfolio. Select pieces that are like other pieces of work that you put in your portfolio earlier in the year. For example, if you already have a lab in your portfolio, add the lab *Volume vs. Number.* Or, if you included a written solution to a problem like *Helipads for Antopolis* from Unit 2 or *Professor Peabody Invents a Ball* from Unit 5, then add *Hour Walk* to your portfolio now. Your teacher may help you make your choices.

6. Add to your Table of Contents. The Table of Contents should include the name of each piece of work, a short description of the work, and the date it was finished.

7. Write a paragraph comparing two pieces of work in your portfolio that are alike in some way. For example, you can compare two labs or your solutions to two problems you have solved. One piece should be new and one should be from earlier in the year. Here are some questions for you to think about as you write your paragraph:

- Which two pieces did you choose to compare?
- How are they alike? How are they different?
- Do you see any improvement in the newest piece of work as compared to the older work? Explain.
- If you could redo the older piece of work, how would you improve it?
- How could you improve the newer piece of work?

8. Write about your favorite piece of work in your portfolio. Tell why you liked it. Explain what you learned from it.

Midyear Experiment and Portfolio Review   SG · Grade 4 · Unit 8 · Lesson 7   233

Student Guide - Page 233

performance on the lab *Perimeter vs. Length* in Unit 2 can be compared to student performance on the lab *Volume vs. Number* in this unit. By reviewing these labs, any improvement in students' abilities to collect, organize, graph, and analyze data will be evident. In the same way, we can look for growth in students' abilities to communicate solutions to problems by comparing student work on earlier assessment tasks to similar work on *Hour Walk* in this unit. These tasks include: *A Letter to Myrna* in Unit 2, *Professor Peabody Invents a Ball* in Unit 5, and *The Broken Calculator* in Unit 7.

Choose at least one more item from this unit that all students will include in their portfolios, then let each student choose one other piece to include.

**TIMS Tip**

Keep the number of items in a portfolio manageable. Ten to twelve well-chosen and chronologically arranged pieces per semester may be most useful. To be able to document growth in mathematical learning over time, include similar items from the beginning, middle, and end of the year.

Suggestions for Teaching the Lesson

Math Facts

- DPP item S provides practice with the multiplication facts using arrays.
- Students use their *Triangle Flash Cards* to study for the *Multiplication Facts Inventory Test*.

Homework and Practice

DPP items Q and R are problems involving money and time. Challenge T provides practice with negative numbers.

Assessment

Students choose work from their collection folders to add to their portfolios to show their mathematical growth over time.

Daily Practice and Problems:
Task & Challenge for Lesson 7

R. Task: Payday (URG p. 19)

Jerome's mother pays him 7¢ for each minute he spends sweeping the floor. He began at 3:45 and finished at 4:17. How much money will he make? Tell the strategies you used to get your answer.

T. Challenge: Changing
Temperatures (URG p. 21)

On Monday, when Irma and her father left Chicago, the temperature was 18°F.

1. When they arrived in Michigan Monday afternoon, the temperature was 20 degrees colder than when they left Chicago. What was the temperature in Michigan on Monday?

2. On Tuesday the high temperature in Michigan was -7°F. How many degrees colder was it on Tuesday than on Monday?

3. The temperature on Wednesday went up to 12°F. The windchill, however, made it feel like 10° below zero. How many degrees colder did the wind make the temperature feel on Wednesday?

AT A GLANCE

Math Facts and Daily Practice and Problems

DPP items Q and R provide practice with money and elapsed time. Bit S provides multiplication facts practice. Challenge T provides practice with negative numbers.

Part 1. Experiment Review

1. *Question 1* on the *Midyear Experiment and Portfolio Review* Activity Pages in the *Student Guide* asks students to make a list of the labs completed so far this year.
2. Choose one lab to review as a class. To guide the review, use *Question 2* in the *Student Guide.*
3. Divide students into groups. Assign one or two labs to each group to review.
4. Compile each group's review information on a transparency of the *Experiment Review Chart* from the *Discovery Assignment Book.* Students record information on their own copies of the *Experiment Review Chart* Activity Pages.
5. Compare and contrast labs using discussion prompts.

Part 2. Portfolio Review

1. *Question 3* in the *Student Guide* asks students to choose items from their collection folders to add to their portfolios.
2. *Questions 4–5* ask students to review the work in their portfolios and to add new pieces from this unit including the *Experiment Review Chart.* Students may choose the items or you can specify which items should be included.
3. Students update their table of contents for their portfolios. *(Question 6)*
4. Students use *Questions 7–8* to help them reflect on their own learning.

Homework

Students review for the *Math Facts Inventory Test* using their *Triangle Flash Cards.*

Notes:

Student Guide

Questions 1–8 (SG pp. 232–233)

See Lesson Guide 7 for a discussion of these questions. See Figure 14 in the Lesson Guide for sample answers to *Question 2.*

Discovery Assignment Book

Experiment Review Chart (DAB pp. 113–114)

*See Figure 14 in the Lesson Guide.

*Answers and/or discussion are included in the Lesson Guide.

**Answers for all the Home Practice in the *Discovery Assignment Book* are at the end of the unit.

LESSON GUIDE

Facts I Know: Multiplication and Division Facts

Estimated Class Sessions: 1

In Part 1 of this lesson students complete their review of the multiplication facts by taking the *Multiplication Facts Inventory Test*. This appears as DPP Bit U.

Part 2 is a brief exploration and review of fact families. In Part 3, students begin their systematic study and assessment of the division facts using *Triangle Flash Cards* and *Division Facts I Know* charts.

Key Content

- Assessing the multiplication facts.
- Self-assessing the division facts for the 5s and 10s.
- Writing the four related number sentences in a fact family.
- Using known multiplication facts to learn related division facts.

Key Vocabulary

divisor
quotient

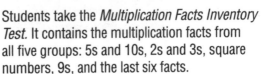

U. Multiplication Facts Inventory Test (URG p. 22)

Students take the *Multiplication Facts Inventory Test*. It contains the multiplication facts from all five groups: 5s and 10s, 2s and 3s, square numbers, 9s, and the last six facts.

We recommend allowing four minutes for this test. Students should have two pens or pencils of different colors ready. During the first four minutes of the test, students write their answers using one color pen or pencil. Encourage students to answer first all the facts they know well and can answer quickly. Then, they should go back and use strategies to solve the rest. After you tell students that four minutes have passed, give them more time to complete the remaining items with the other color pen or pencil.

Students update their *Multiplication Facts I Know* charts using the results of the test.

DPP Task is on page 99. Suggestions for using the DPPs are on page 99.

Curriculum Sequence

Before This Unit

Grade 3 Units 11–20 included systematic practice and assessment of the multiplication facts.

In Grade 4 Unit 3, students began systematically reviewing the multiplication facts and using their knowledge of the multiplication facts to develop strategies for learning the division facts.

After This Unit

In Unit 9, students will use the *Triangle Flash Cards: 5s* and *10s* to practice the division facts. Students will continue practicing the multiplication and division facts in small groups, throughout Units 9–16. In Unit 16, their fluency with the division facts will be assessed with an inventory test. See the Daily Practice and Problems Guide for Unit 9 for information on the distribution of division facts practice and assessment.

Materials List

Print Materials for Students

		Math Facts and Daily Practice and Problems	Assessment Activity	Written Assessment
Student Books	**Student Guide**		*Facts I Know: Multiplication and Division Facts* Pages 234–236	
	Discovery Assignment Book		*Triangle Flash Cards: 5s* Page 115, *Triangle Flash Cards: 10s* Page 117, and *Division Facts I Know* chart Page 119	
Teacher Resources	**Facts Resource Guide** ⊙	DPP Items 8U & 8V Use *Triangle Flash Cards: 5s* and *Triangle Flash Cards: 10s* to practice division facts for 5s and 10s.	*Division Facts I Know* chart	DPP Item 8U *Multiplication Facts Inventory Test*
	Unit Resource Guide	DPP Items U–V Pages 22–23 ⊙		DPP Item U *Multiplication Facts Inventory Test* Pages 22 & 24 ⊙
	Generic Section ⊙		*Dot Paper*, *Triangle Flash Cards: 5s*, and *Triangle Flash Cards: 10s*, 1 each per student (optional)	

⊙   available on Teacher Resource CD

All Transparency Masters, Blackline Masters, and Assessment Blackline Masters in the Unit Resource Guide are on the Teacher Resource CD.

Supplies for Each Student

scissors, optional
ruler, optional
envelope for storing flash cards

Materials for the Teacher

Transparency of *Triangle Flash Cards: 5s* Activity Page (Discovery Assignment Book) Page 115
Transparency of *Triangle Flash Cards: 10s* Activity Page (Discovery Assignment Book) Page 117
Transparency of *Division Facts I Know* Activity Page (Discovery Assignment Book) Page 119
Observational Assessment Record (Unit Resource Guide, Pages 7–8 and Teacher Resource CD)
Individual Assessment Record Sheet (Teacher Implementation Guide, Assessment section and Teacher Resource CD)

Before the Activity

Part 3 of this lesson introduces students to the use of *Triangle Flash Cards* to practice division facts. The *Triangle Flash Cards: 5s* and *10s* are located in the *Discovery Assignment Book* for this lesson. Have students cut out the cards and place them in envelopes.

TIMS Tip

For more durable flash cards, copy the *Triangle Flash Cards* in the Generic Section onto card stock or laminate the cards. You can give students two sets of cards so that they can take a set home and leave a set at school.

Part 1. *Multiplication Facts Inventory Test*

Students take the test as described in DPP Bit U. Allow four minutes for the test. At the end of the four minutes, have students change pencils and finish the test. Students update their *Multiplication Facts I Know* charts.

Have students discuss strategies for any remaining facts that they do not know well and record the strategies in their journals. Students can continue to practice these facts with *Triangle Flash Cards* at home.

Part 2. Picturing Fact Families

Students review fact families through the use of grids (arrays). By this time, most students will be comfortable with fact families and can review this section quickly. For students who are still struggling with the concept, this exercise provides a visual image to help develop their understanding. These students may benefit from drawing the two grids on a piece of centimeter dot paper. Students first examine and draw a grid divided into 20 squares by making 4 rows *(Question 1)*. Next they examine and draw a grid divided into 20 squares by making 5 rows *(Question 2)*. They write the appropriate number sentence on each rectangle they have drawn, using the number of rows as the divisor. Ask students:

- *What multiplication sentence describes each rectangle?*

- *Write that multiplication sentence on the rectangle with the division sentence.*

Have students cut out the rectangles they have drawn on grid paper. By rotating one and placing it on the other, they will see that both grids are the same. All four number sentences ($5 \times 4 = 20$, $4 \times 5 = 20$, $20 \div 5 = 4$, $20 \div 4 = 5$) describe the same rectangle. All are related and belong to the same fact family.

Facts I Know: Multiplication and Division Facts

Picturing Fact Families

1. The picture below represents the following problem: If a rectangle has a total of 20 squares in 4 rows, how many squares are in each row?

What division sentence describes this problem?

2. The picture below represents the following problem: If a rectangle has a total of 20 squares in 5 rows, how many squares are in each row?

A. What division sentence describes this problem?
B. These two division sentences are members of the same **fact family**. What are the other number sentences that are in this same fact family?

3. Solve the given fact. Then name other facts in the same fact family.
   A. $9 \times 7 = ?$ B. $6 \times 4 = ?$ C. $7 \times 8 = ?$

Division Facts and *Triangle Flash Cards*

4. The directions that follow tell you how to use your *Triangle Flash Cards* to practice the division facts. Work with a partner. Use your *Triangle Flash Cards: 5s* and *10s*.

234 SG · Grade 4 · Unit 8 · Lesson 8   Facts I Know

Student Guide - Page 234

A. One partner covers the number in the square. This number will be the answer to a division problem. The answer to a division problem is called the **quotient**. The number in the circle is the **divisor**. The divisor is the number that divides the largest number on the flash card. The second person solves a division fact with the two uncovered numbers as shown below.

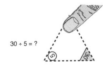

$30 \div 5 = ?$

B. Place each flash card in one of three piles: those facts you know well and can answer quickly, those that you can figure out with a strategy, and those that you need to learn.

C. Begin your *Division Facts I Know* chart. Circle the facts you know well and can answer quickly.
For example, Jacob knew $30 \div 5 = 6$. 5 is the divisor, so Jacob circled the 30 in the row for a divisor of 5.

Division Facts I Know

×	0	1	2	3	4	5	6	7	8	9	10
0	0	0	0	0	0	0	0	0	0	0	0
1	0	1	2	3	4	5	6	7	8	9	10
2	0	2	4	6	8	10	12	14	16	18	20
3	0	3	6	9	12	15	18	21	24	27	30
4	0	4	8	12	16	20	24	28	32	36	40
5	0	5	10	15	20	25	⃝30	35	40	45	50
6	0	6	12	18	24	30	36	42	48	54	60
7	0	7	14	21	28	35	42	49	56	63	70
8	0	8	16	24	32	40	48	56	64	72	80
9	0	9	18	27	36	45	54	63	72	81	90
10	0	10	20	30	40	50	60	70	80	90	100

Divisor

Recording $30 \div 5 = 6$ as a Fact I Know.

Facts I Know   SG · Grade 4 · Unit 8 · Lesson 8 235

Student Guide - Page 235

Daily Practice and Problems: Task for Lesson 8

V. Task: More Facts Practice

(URG p. 23)

Find the number for *n* that will make each number sentence true. Then write the other number sentences in the same fact family.

A. $n \times 7 = 42$

B. $56 \div n = 8$

C. $20 \div n = 5$

D. $9 \times n = 72$

E. $64 \div n = 8$

F. $n \div 4 = 7$

Find the number for *n* that will make each number sentence true.

G. $7 \times n = 2800$

H. $n \times 40 = 2000$

I. $800 \times n = 72{,}000$

J. $n \times 70 = 350$

Suggestions for Teaching the Lesson

Math Facts

DPP Task V provides practice with using multiplication facts to complete number sentences and to multiply numbers that end in zero. It also provides practice with division facts.

Assessment

- DPP Bit U is the *Multiplication Facts Inventory Test*. Have students change pens or pencils after four minutes. Record students' progress with the multiplication facts on the *Observational Assessment Record*.

- Transfer appropriate documentation from the Unit 8 *Observational Assessment Record* to students' *Individual Assessment Record Sheets*.

AT A GLANCE

Math Facts and Daily Practice and Problems

DPP Bit U is the *Multiplication Facts Inventory Test.* Task V provides practice with multiplication and division facts.

Part 1. *Multiplication Facts Inventory Test*

Students take the *Multiplication Facts Inventory Test* in DPP item U. Allow four minutes for the test. Then let students change to a different pen and finish the test. Students update their *Multiplication Facts I Know* charts.

Part 2. Picturing Fact Families

1. Students read and discuss the Picturing Fact Families section in the *Student Guide.*
2. Students draw and cut out two 5×4 rectangles on dot paper. (optional)
3. Students list the four fact families that describe a 5×4 rectangle.

Part 3. Division Facts and Triangle Flash Cards

1. Students read the Division Facts and *Triangle Flash Cards* section in the *Student Guide.*
2. Discuss with the students how to use the *Triangle Flash Cards* to practice division facts, by first covering the numbers in the squares and then covering the numbers in the circles.
3. Show the transparency of a *Division Facts I Know* chart.
4. Model marking a *Division Facts I Know* chart with a sample division fact.

Assessment

1. Use the *Multiplication Facts Inventory Test* in DPP Bit U and the *Observational Assessment Record* to document students' fluency with the multiplication facts.
2. Transfer appropriate documentation from the Unit 8 *Observational Assessment Record* to the students' *Individual Assessment Record Sheets.*

Notes:

Student Guide

Questions 1–5 (SG pp. 234–236)

1. $20 \div 4 = 5$
2. **A.** $20 \div 5 = 4$
   B. $4 \times 5 = 20; 5 \times 4 = 20$

3. **A.** $63; 7 \times 9 = 63; 63 \div 7 = 9; 63 \div 9 = 7$
   B. $24; 4 \times 6 = 24; 24 \div 4 = 6; 24 \div 6 = 4$
   C. $56; 8 \times 7 = 56; 56 \div 8 = 7; 56 \div 7 = 8$
4.–5. *

*Answers and/or discussion are included in the Lesson Guide.
**Answers for all the Home Practice in the *Discovery Assignment Book* are at the end of the unit.

Discovery Assignment Book

Part 2. Number Relationships

Questions 1–3 (DAB p. 93)

Explanations will vary for Questions 1 and 2.

1. **A.** No. $3 \times 17 = 51$

   B. Yes. Its only factors are 1 and 53.

   C. No. $55 \div 5 = 11$

2. **A.** Yes. 6 divides 96 evenly; $96 \div 6 = 16$;
   The sum of the digits of 96 ($9 + 6 = 15$)
   is a multiple of 3. 96 is also an even
   number. Since it is divisible by 2 and 3,
   it is divisible by 6.

   B. No. 6 does not divide 116 evenly;
   $116 \div 6 = 19.333$ . . . See explanation
   for 2A.

3. Answers will vary. One possible factor
   tree is shown.

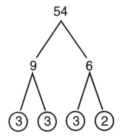

Part 3. Performing Operations

Questions 1–5 (DAB p. 94)

1. **A.** 1228

   B. 6576

   C. 4296

   D. 190

   E. 63,000

   F. 264

2. $262

3. Estimates will vary. $30 \times 70 = 2100$ points

4. Estimates will vary.
   $45,000,000 - 40,000,000 = 5,000,000$ votes

5. 88 days

Part 4. Arithmetic Review

Questions 1–3 (DAB p. 95)

1. **A.** 5181

   B. 512

   C. 376

   D. 1918

   E. 1560

   F. 410

2. Possible strategy: $50 \times 8 = 400$

3. **A.** Answers will vary. She has enough money:
   $3.25 + $3.00 + $1.50 = $7.75. She will
   receive about $2.25 in change.

   B. Answers will vary. She has enough money.
   She will receive between $5.00 and $7.00
   in change.

   C. $3.74

Part 5. Base-Ten Shorthand

Questions 1–2 (DAB p. 96)

1. **A.** 2045

   B. 254

   C. 1158

   D. 2100; Numbers in order: 254, 1158,
   2045, 2100

2. **A.** 1,430,000; 9,104,000; 10,435,000;
   14,001,000; 23,247,000; 25,928,000

   B. Estimates will vary.
   $14,000,000 - 3,000,000 = 11,000,000$ men

   C. Estimates will vary.
   $23,000,000 - 12,000,000 = 11,000,000$
   women

*Answers and/or discussion are included in the Lesson Guide.